CHAPTER
17 Plane Shapes

What plane shapes do you see?

SCHOOL HOME CONNECTION

Dear Family,
Today we started Chapter 17. We will identify plane shapes, count sides and corners of shapes, and learn about congruence and symmetry. Here is the math vocabulary and an activity for us to do together at home.

Love,

____

My Math Words

line of symmetry
symmetry
flip
slide
turn
corner

Vocabulary

line of symmetry

This butterfly has **symmetry** because both sides match.

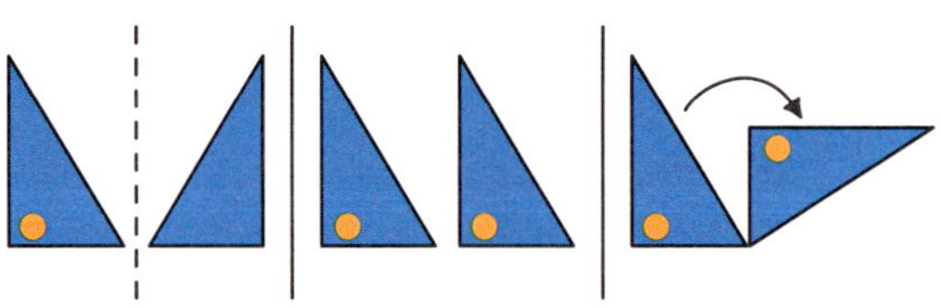

flip **slide** **turn**

corner The point where two sides of a shape meet. Also called a vertex.

Visit *The Learning Site* for additional ideas and activities. www.harcourtschool.com

ACTIVITY

Have your child cut from construction paper a circle, square, and triangle. Work with your child to make a pattern on another paper, tracing the shapes. Your child may wish to color the design you make together.

Books to Share

To read about plane shapes with your child, look for these books in your local library.

The Village of Round and Square Houses, by Ann Grifalconi, Little, Brown and Company, 1986.

Rectangles, by David L. Stienecker, Marshall Cavendish, 1997.

Name ____________________

Identify Plane Shapes

circles squares triangles rectangles ovals

1 Color the circles. Cross out the shapes that are not circles.

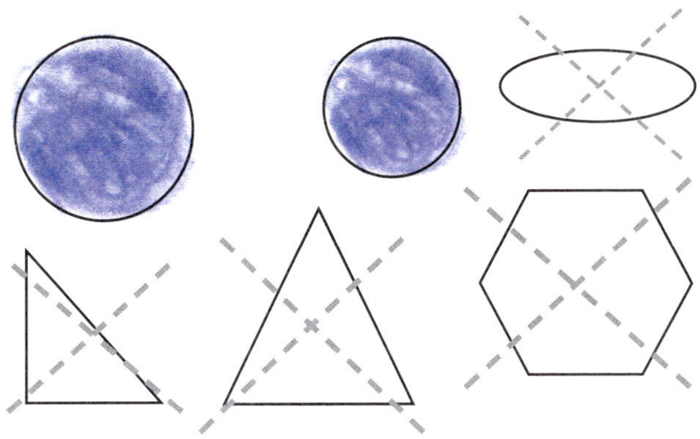

2 Color the squares. Cross out the shapes that are not squares.

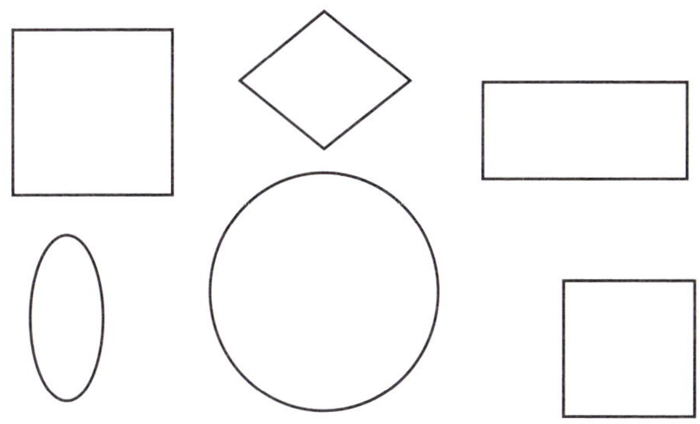

3 Color the triangles. Cross out the shapes that are not triangles.

4 Color the rectangles. Cross out the shapes that are not rectangles.

Talk About It ▪ Reasoning

How are circles and ovals different from triangles, squares, and rectangles?

Practice

Follow the directions to decorate.

1. Draw 3 squares. Color them blue.
2. Draw 5 circles. Color them red.
3. Draw 4 triangles. Color them green.
4. Draw 2 ovals. Color them orange.

5. Draw 4 rectangles. Color them blue.
6. Draw 5 circles. Color them green.
7. Draw 2 triangles. Color them yellow.
8. Draw 3 squares. Color them orange.

Problem Solving ■ Visual Thinking

9. How many dots are inside the rectangle but not inside the triangle?

_______ dots

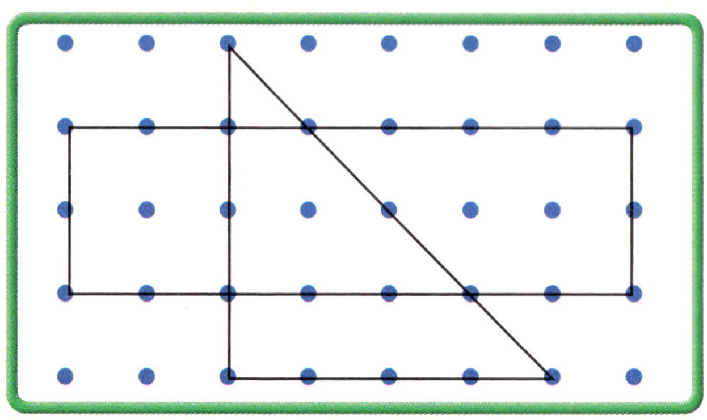

HOME ACTIVITY • Give your child paper and pencil, and have him or her draw a picture made up of plane figures.

Name ______________________

Sides and Corners

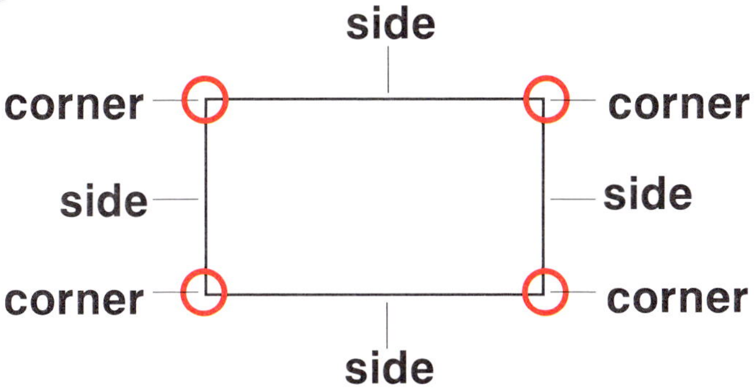

This shape has 4 **sides** and 4 **corners**.

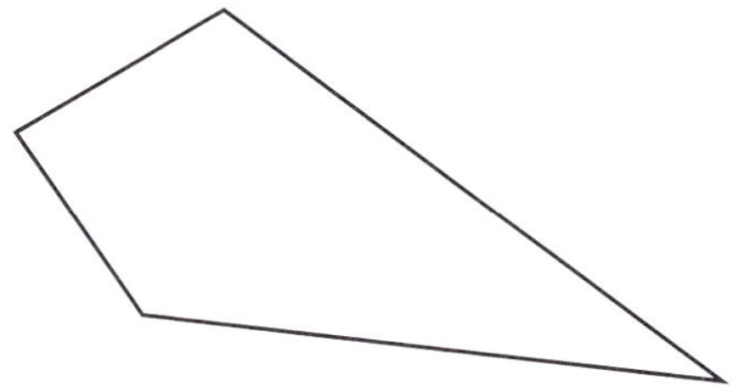

This shape has 4 sides and 4 corners.

Write how many sides and corners.

1. 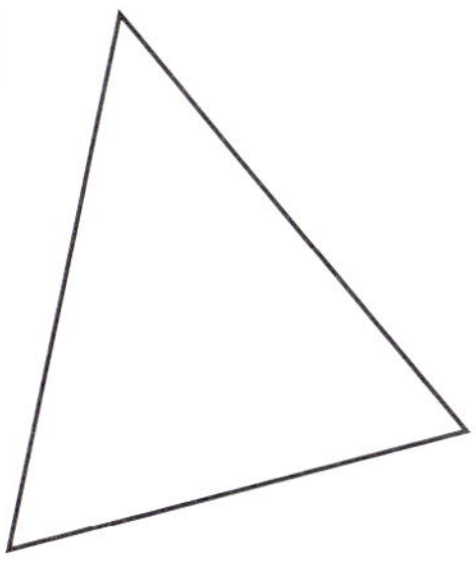
_____ sides
_____ corners

2. 
_____ sides
_____ corners

3. 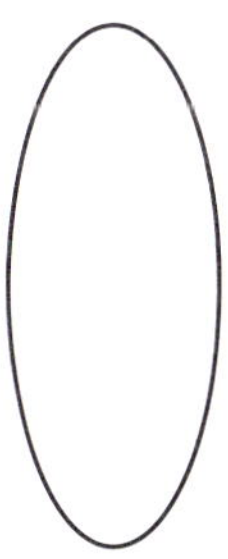
_____ sides
_____ corners

4. 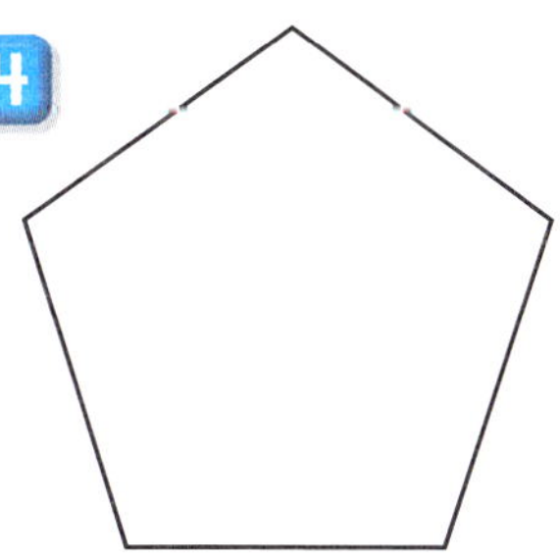
_____ sides
_____ corners

5. 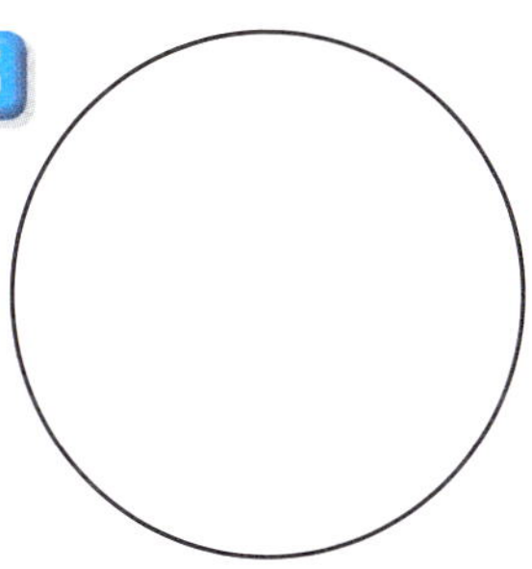
_____ sides
_____ corners

6. 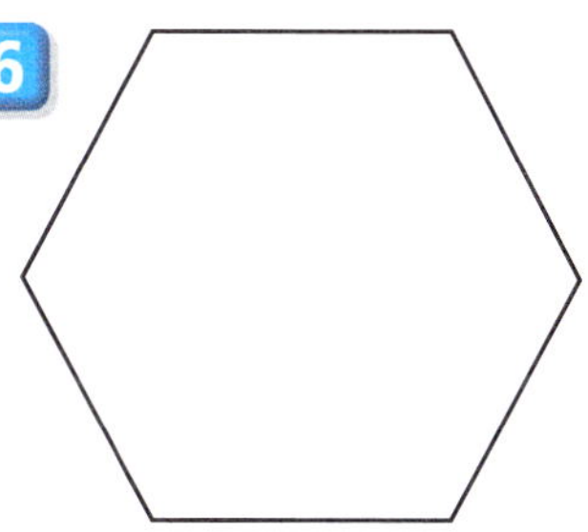
_____ sides
_____ corners

Talk About It ■ Reasoning

Which two shapes have 0 sides and 0 corners? Explain why.

Practice

Draw the shape.

1. 6 sides 6 corners

2. 3 sides 3 corners

3. 4 sides 4 corners
2 sides are long.
2 sides are short.

4. 4 sides 4 corners
All 4 sides are the same length.

Problem Solving ▪ Visual Thinking

5. Draw a shape that has sides and corners.
Cover it. Tell a classmate how to draw it.

your drawing | your classmate's drawing

HOME ACTIVITY • Give your child a matching number of sides and corners, such as 4 sides and 4 corners. Have him or her draw the shape.

Name ______________________________

Congruence and Symmetry

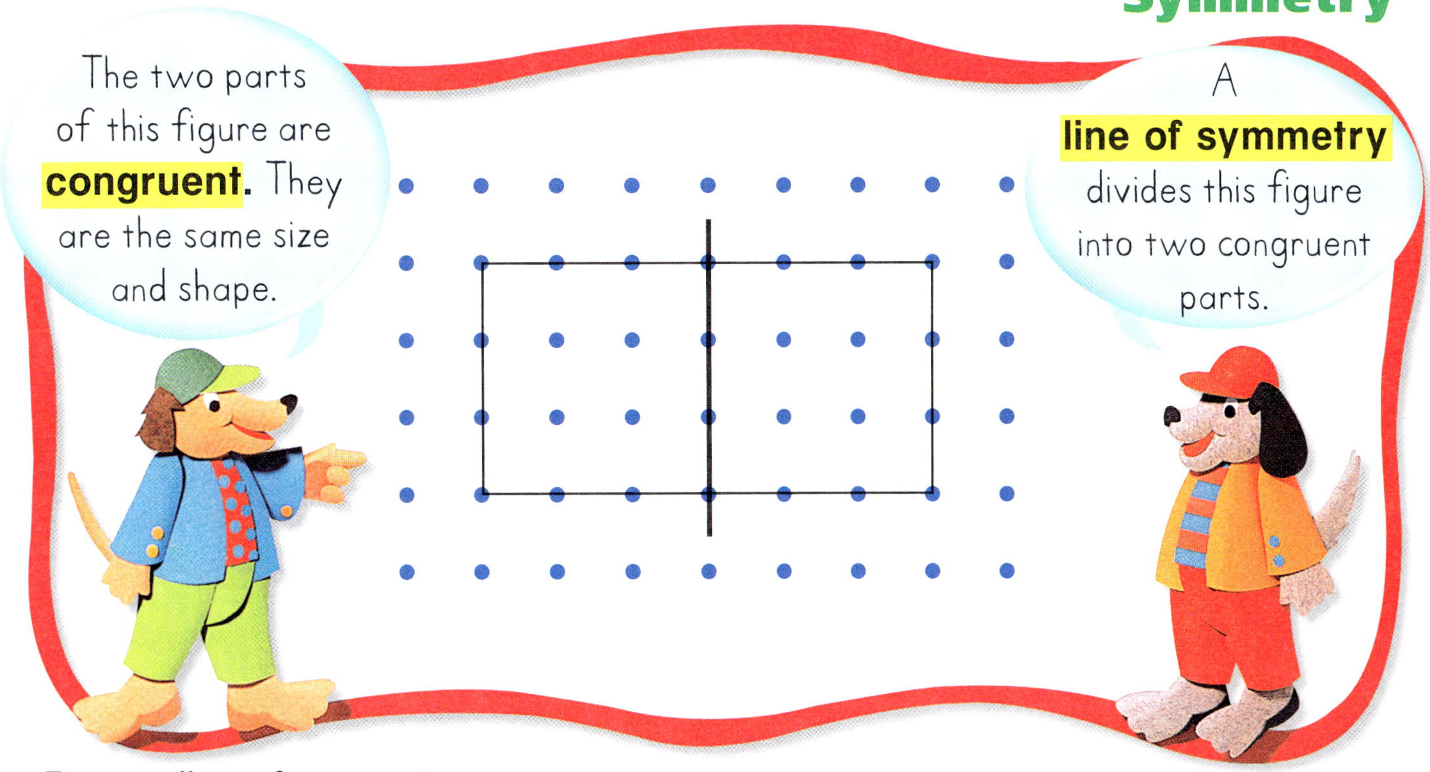

Draw a line of symmetry.
The two parts will be congruent.

1 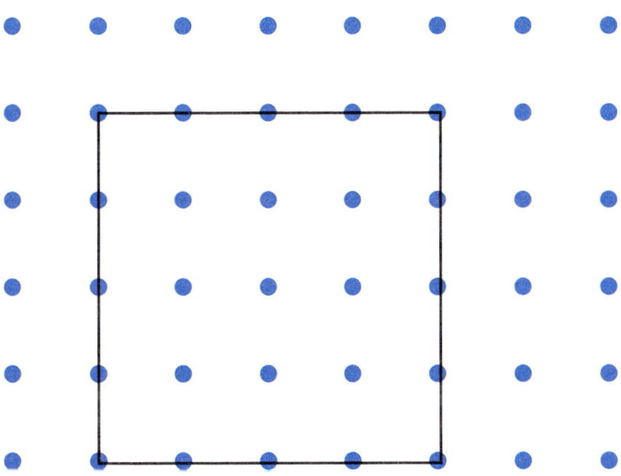

2 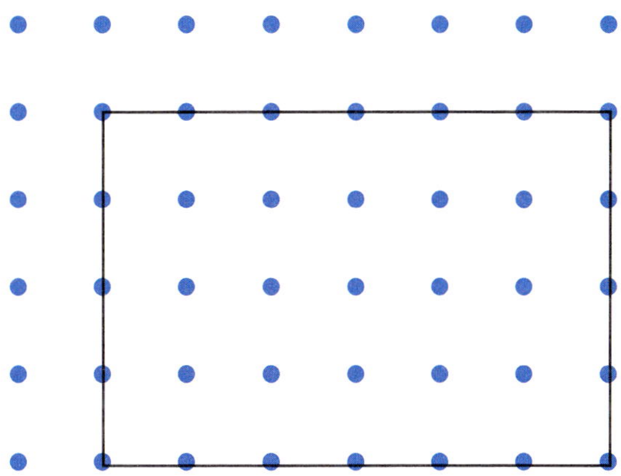

3 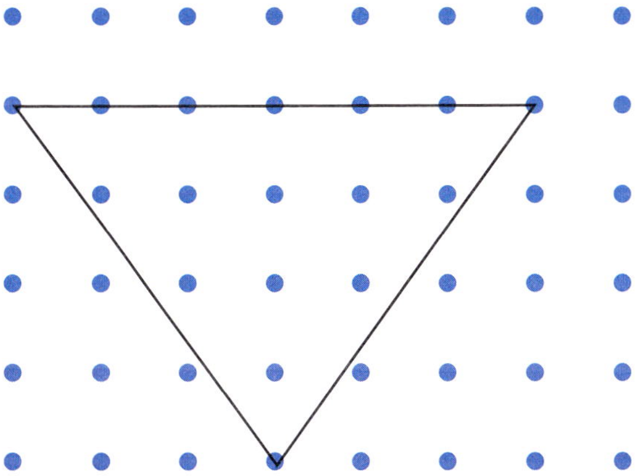

4 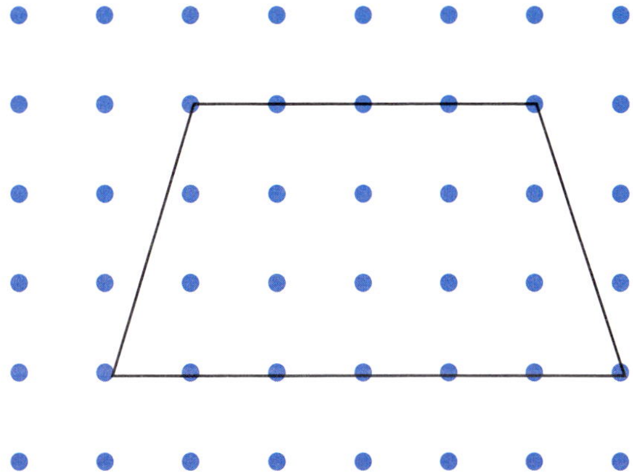

Talk About It ■ Reasoning

How can you prove that the two parts of a figure are congruent?

Practice

Draw a line of symmetry.
The two parts will be congruent.

1 

2 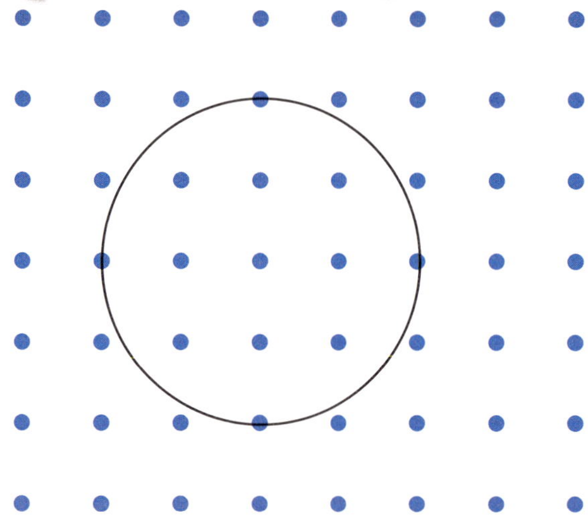

3 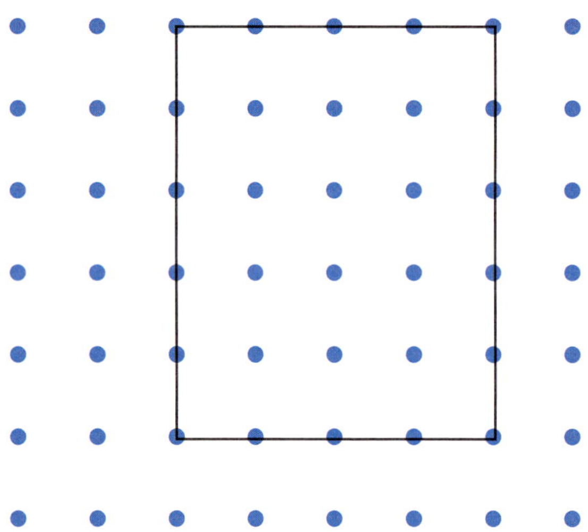

4 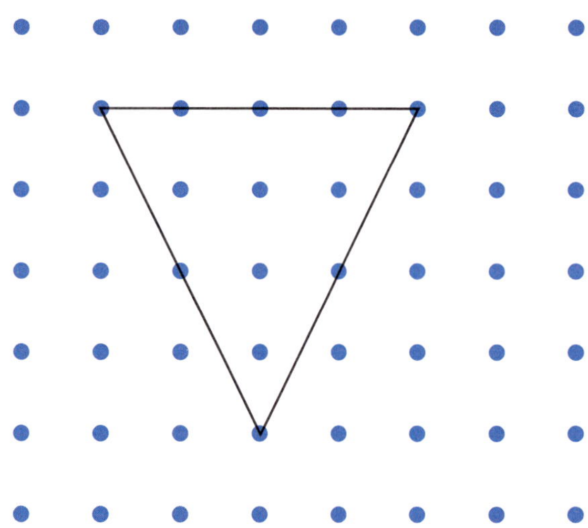

Mixed Review

Add or subtract.

5

63¢	52¢	22	18	51	37
− 47¢	− 37¢	+ 16	+ 9	− 19	− 28

HOME ACTIVITY • Draw and cut out a shape. Have your child use your shape to draw and cut out a shape that is the same size and shape.

Name ______________________

UNDERSTAND PLAN SOLVE CHECK

Problem Solving
Make a Model

Chris wants to make a rectangle. How can he use 2 squares to make a rectangle?

UNDERSTAND

What do you want to find out?

PLAN

You can make a model to solve the problem.

SOLVE

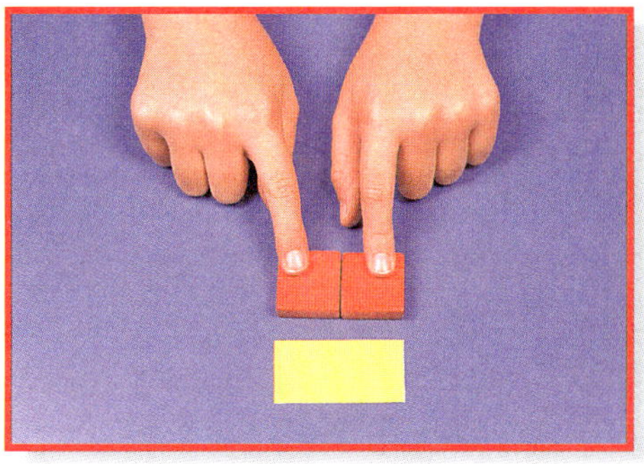

CHECK

Does your answer makes sense? Explain.

Use plane shapes. Put them together to make a new shape. Draw it. Write the name of the shape you made.

1 2 triangles

rectangle

2 2 rectangles

____

Practice

Draw a line or lines to separate the shape into new shapes.

1

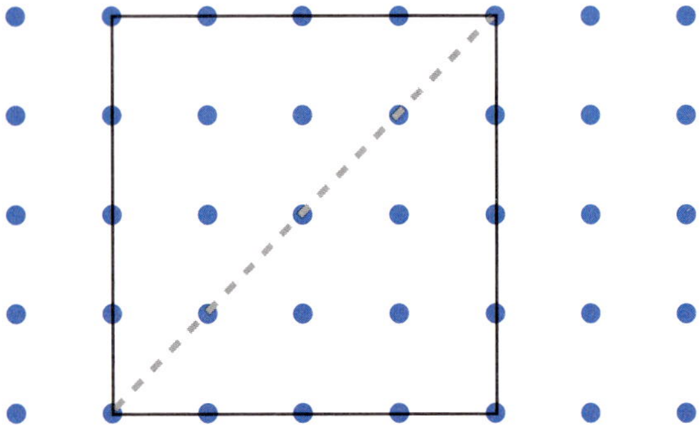

2 triangles

2

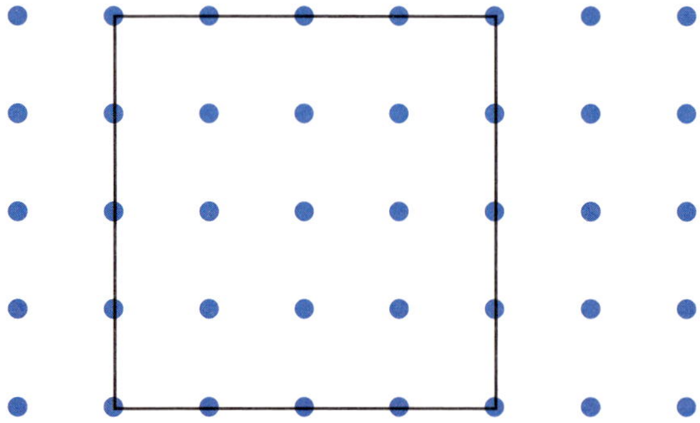

4 squares

3

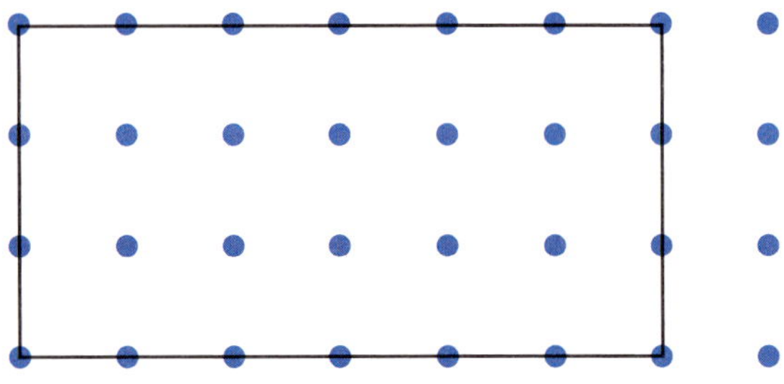

2 triangles

4

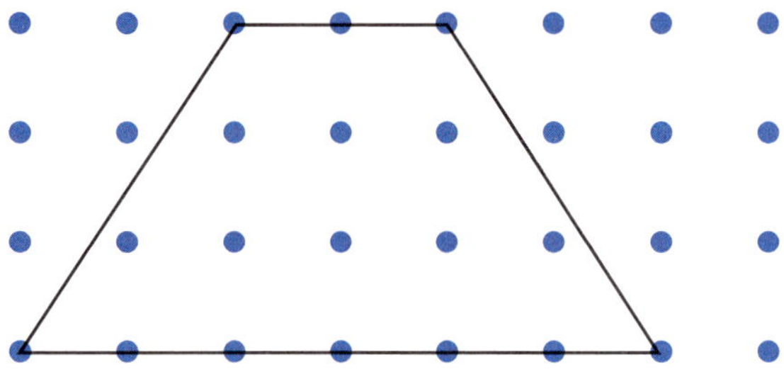

3 triangles

5

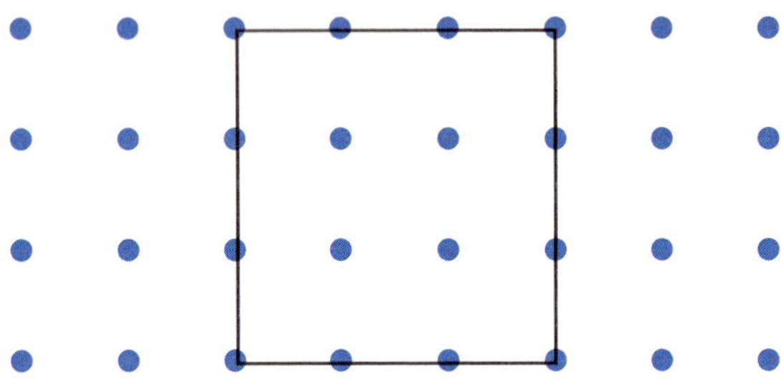

4 triangles

6

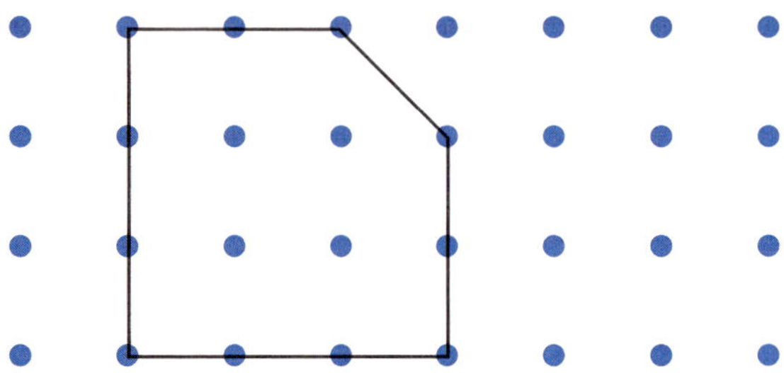

3 triangles

Mixed Review

Write <, >, or =.

7 37 ◯ 54   42 ◯ 42   83 ◯ 25

8 83 ◯ 99   94 ◯ 49   21 ◯ 78

HOME ACTIVITY • Draw and cut out a shape. Have your child draw lines on your figure and cut it apart to make and name new shapes.

Name ______________________________

Moving Shapes

Hands On

You can move your box of crayons by turning it or flipping it.

You can **turn**.

You can **flip**.

Use ◣.
Put your ◣ on top of the first one.
Do not lift your ◣. Turn it to fit on top of the second ◣. Trace the shape.

1

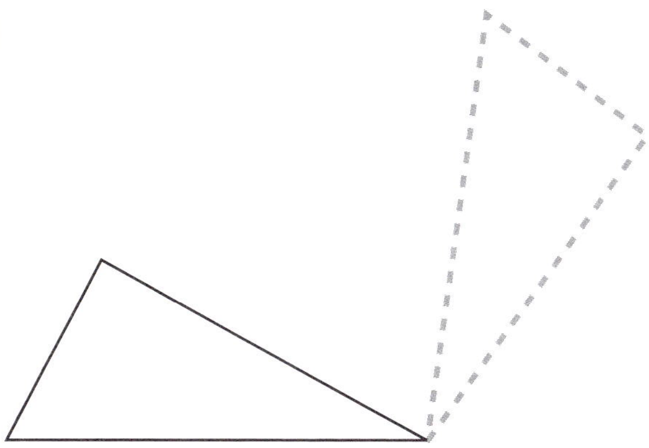

2

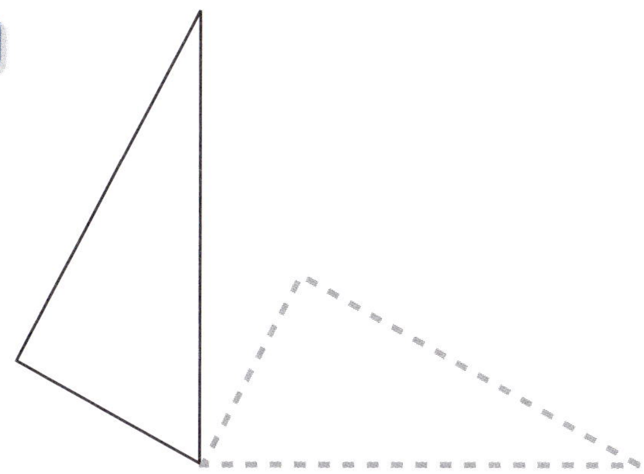

Put your ◣ on top of the first one.
Flip it to fit on top of the second ◣.
Trace the shape.

3

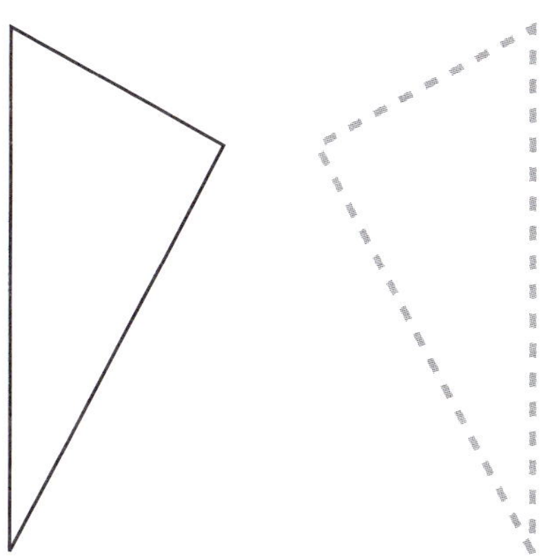

4

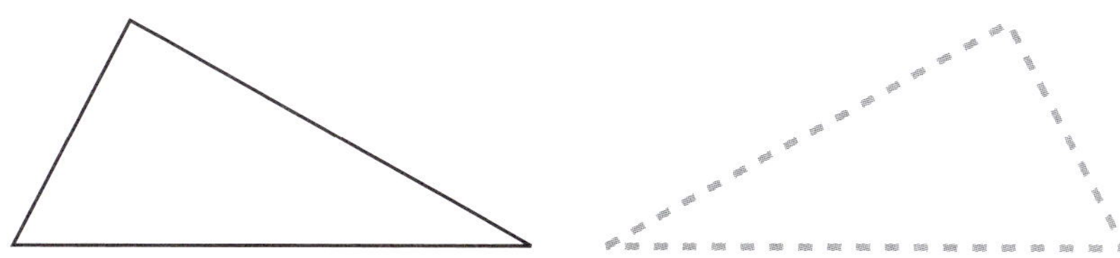

Talk About It ■ **Reasoning**

How is a turn different from a flip?

Practice

flip

turn

Use  .

Move the  the same way as shown in the picture.

Circle flip or turn to tell how you moved it.

1

flip turn

2

flip turn

3

flip turn

4

flip turn

5

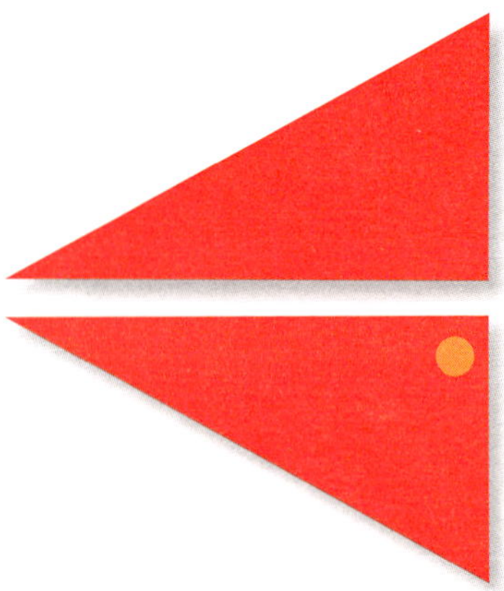

flip turn

6

flip turn

HOME ACTIVITY • Ask your child to draw and cut out a shape. Have him or her show how to flip and turn the shape.

Name ______________________________

More About Moving Shapes

Hands On

You can **slide**.

Use plane shapes. Put your plane shape on top of the one shown. Slide it to a different place. Trace to show the new place. Draw the dot.

1

2

3

4

5

6

Talk About It ■ Reasoning

How is a slide different from a turn? How is it the same?

Practice

Write the word that names the move.

1 

flip

2 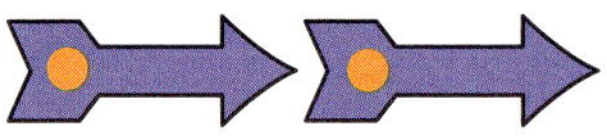

3 

4 

5 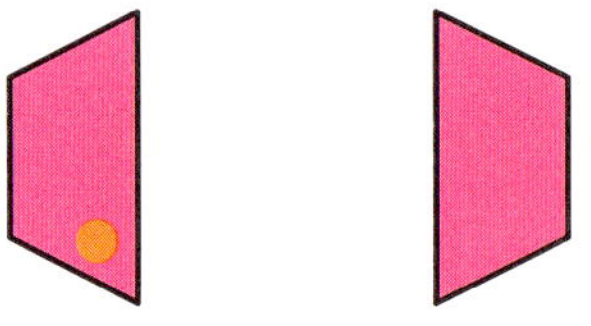

6 

7 

8 

9 

Algebra

Draw two more  to continue the most likely pattern.

10 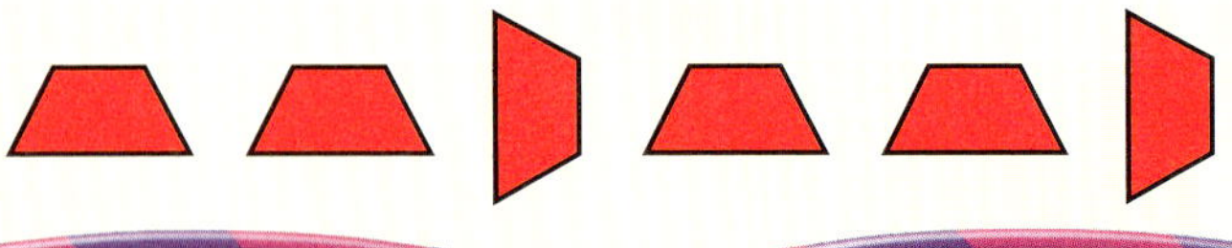

HOME ACTIVITY • Put together a jigsaw puzzle with your child. Have him or her tell you which kind of move made each piece fit.

Name ______________________

Review/Test
Chapter 17

CHECK ▪ Concepts and Skills

Color the triangles. Cross out the shapes that are not triangles.

1 

Write how many sides and corners.

2 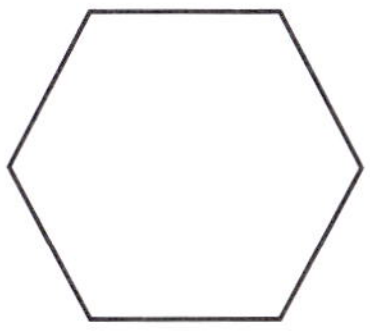

______ sides

______ corners

Draw a line of symmetry. The two parts will be congruent.

3 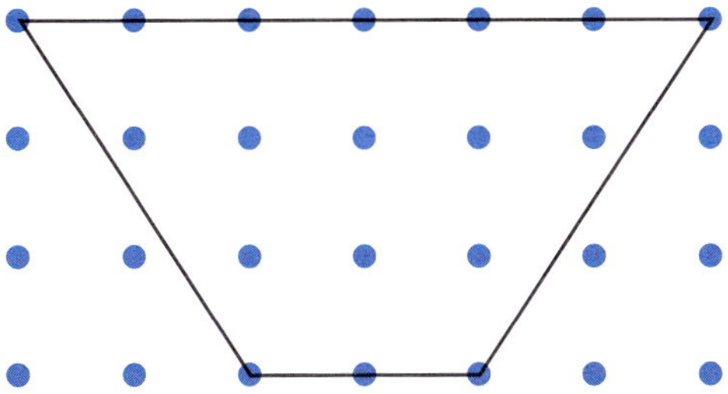

4 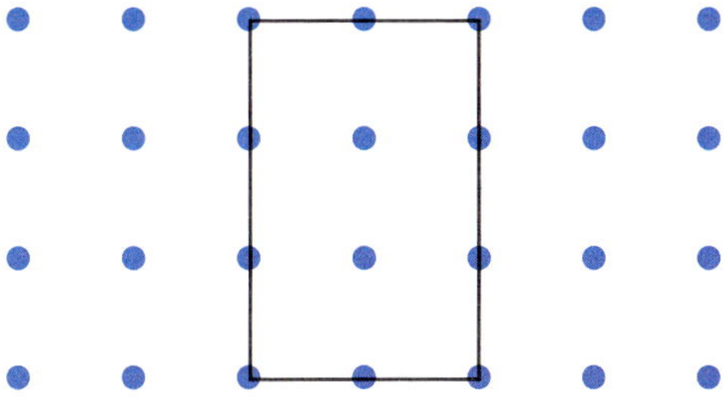

Circle the word that names the move.

5 

flip slide

6 

flip slide

CHECK ▪ Problem Solving

Use plane shapes. Put them together to make a new shape. Draw it. Write the name of the shape you made.

7

two triangles

____

Name ______________________

Standardized Test Prep
Chapters 1–17

Choose the best answer for questions 1–4.

1 Which is a rectangle?

2 Which shows a line of symmetry?

3 Which shape can be made from two triangles?

4 Which shows a flip?

Show What You Know

5 Draw two different shapes that each have 3 sides and 3 corners.

CHAPTER 18 Solid Figures

What solid figures can you find in this picture?

SCHOOL HOME CONNECTION

Dear Family,

Today we started Chapter 18. We will identify and use solid figures. Here is the math vocabulary and an activity for us to do at home.

Love,

____

My Math Words

rectangular prism
sphere
cone
cylinder
pyramid
cube

Vocabulary

rectangular prism

sphere

cone

cylinder

pyramid

cube

ACTIVITY

Play a game of I Spy with your child. Look around the room for an object that is shaped like a solid figure. Give your child clues about the object you have in mind. Your child should name the object and tell you what solid figure it is, using the correct math word.

Books to Share

To read about geometry with your child, look for these books in your local library.

The Goat in the Rug,
by Charles L. Blood
and Martin Link,
Simon and Schuster, 1990.

Shapes,
by Philip Yenawine,
Delacorte, 1991.

Visit *The Learning Site* for additional ideas and activities. www.harcourtschool.com

Name ________________________________

Identify Solid Figures

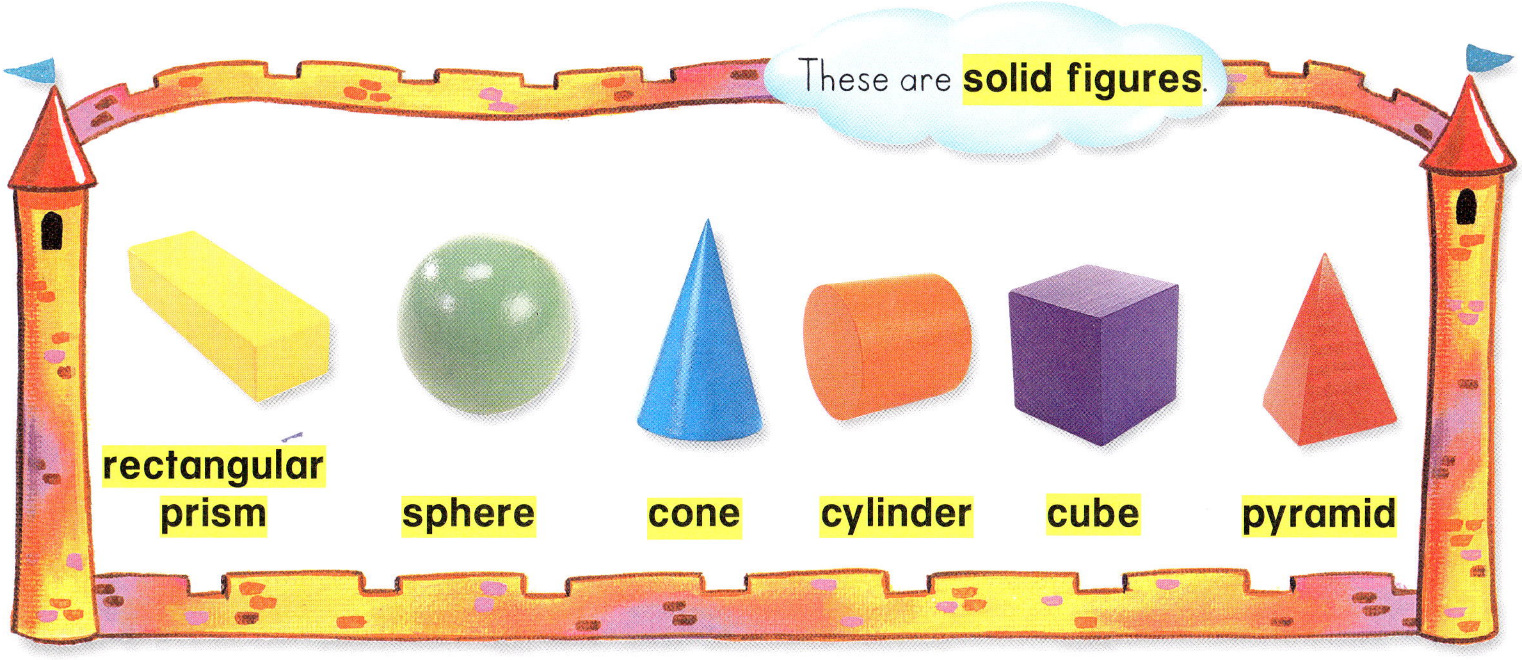

Color the objects that are close to the shape of the solid figure.
Cross out the objects that are not shaped like the solid figure.

Talk About It ■ **Reasoning**

Which figures might roll if they are placed on a table?
Does it depend on how they are put on the table? Explain.

Practice

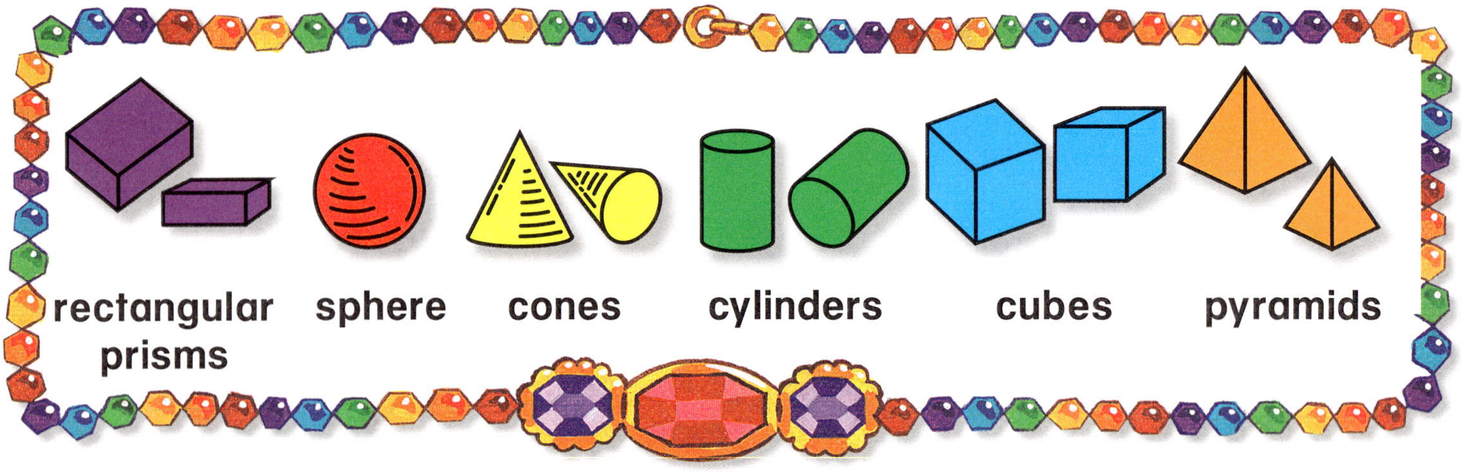

Color the figures that are the same shape.

1
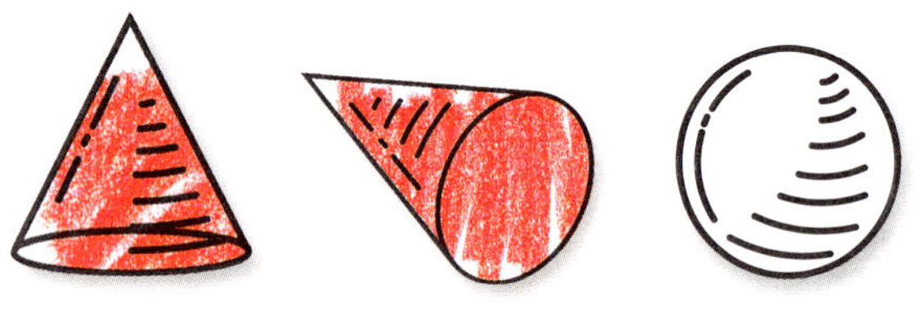

2

3

4
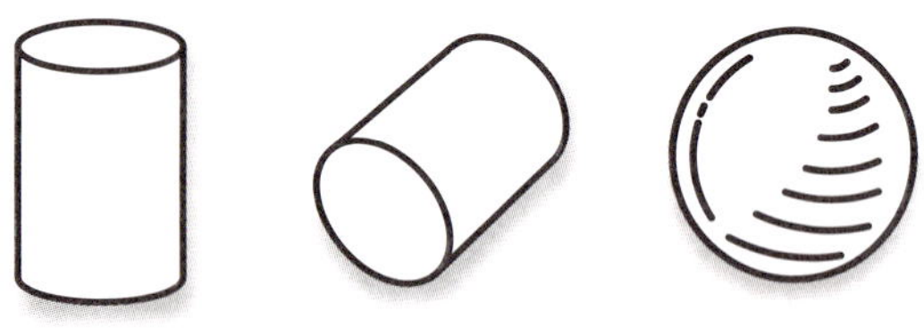

5
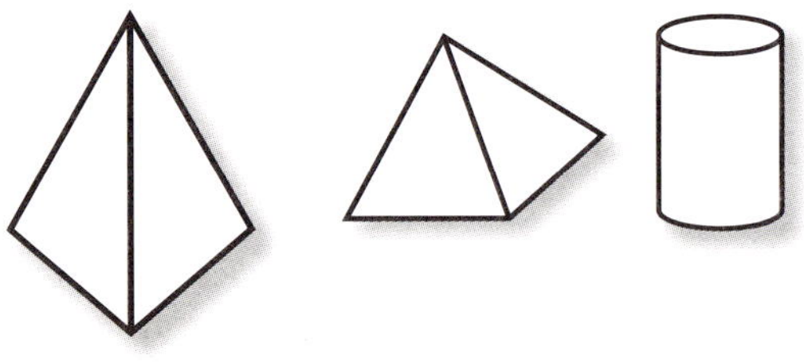

6

Problem Solving ■ Reasoning

7 Is every cube also a rectangular prism? Is every rectangular prism also a cube? Draw examples. Then explain your thinking.

HOME ACTIVITY • Have your child point out objects that are shaped like the solid figures he or she has learned about.

Name ________________________________

Make Plane Shapes

Hands On

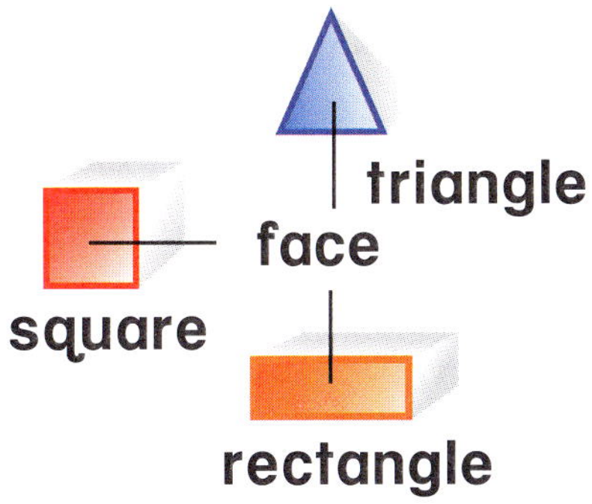

Use figures. Trace the faces. Then circle a plane shape you can trace from the solid figure. Write the name of the plane shape.

1. 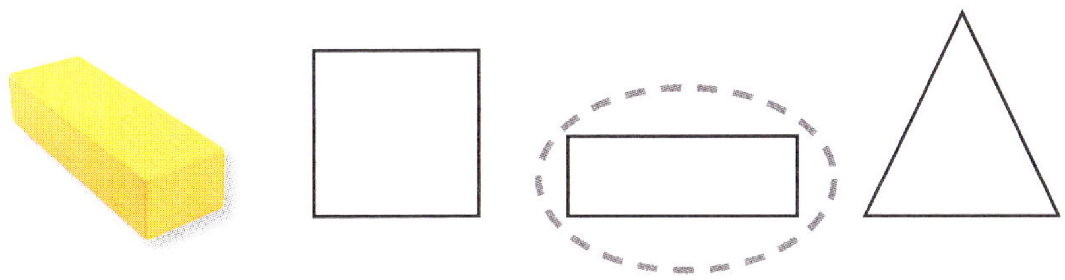

   rectangle

2. 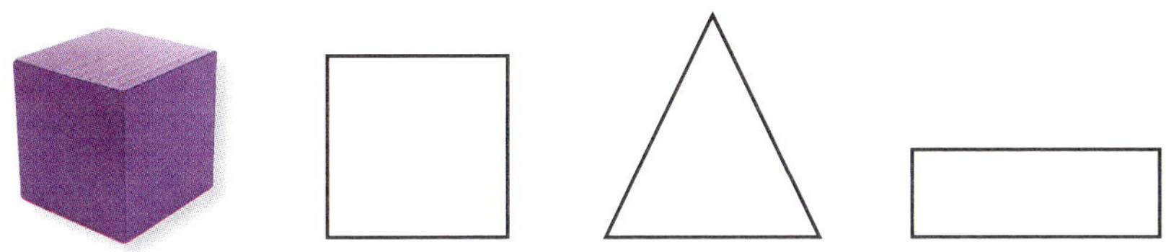

   ____

3. 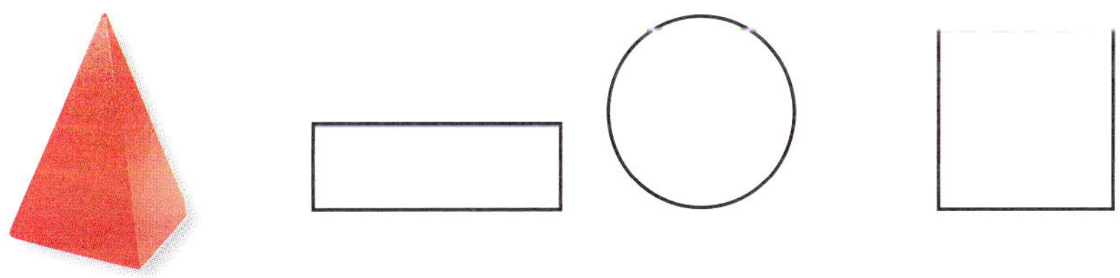

   ____

4. 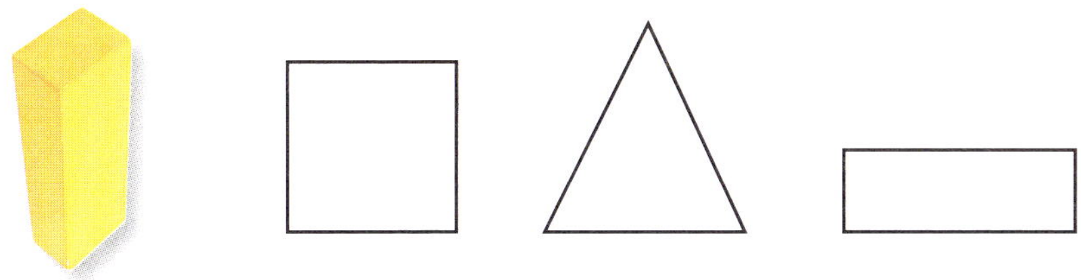

   ____

5. 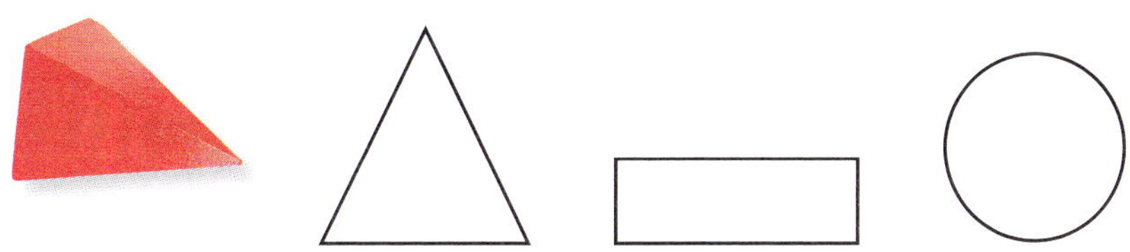

   ____

Practice

Look at the faces on each solid figure. Circle the solid figure you can use to trace the shapes.

1

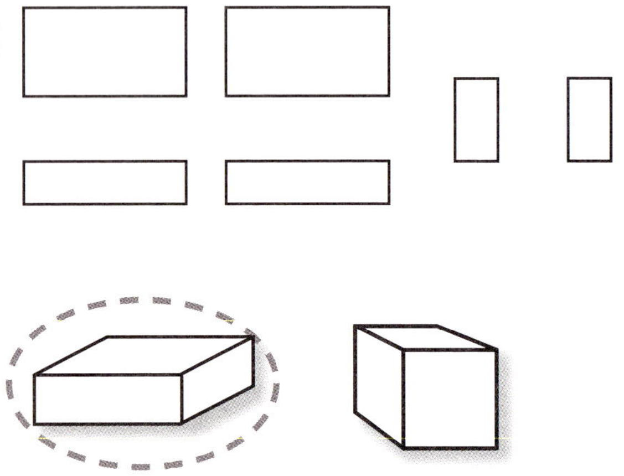

2

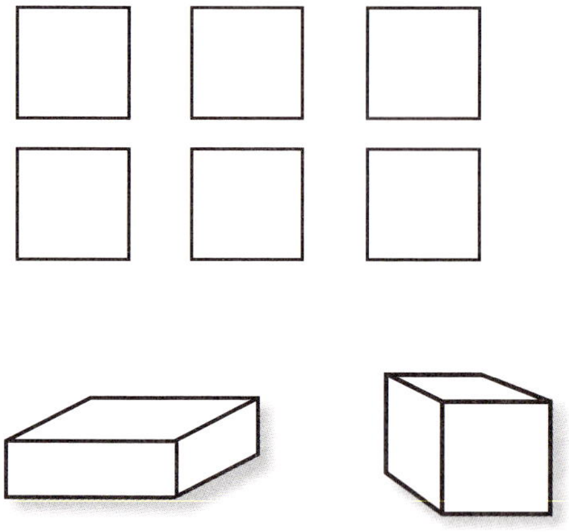

3

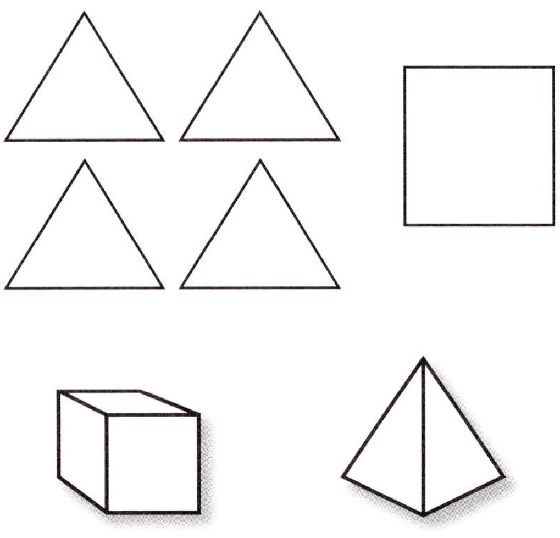

4

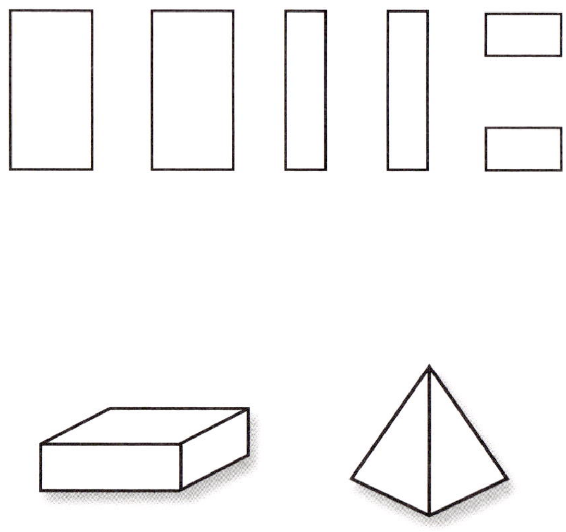

Problem Solving ■ Visual Thinking

Circle the solid figure that is missing.

5

6

HOME ACTIVITY • Gather objects that are shaped like solid figures your child knows. Have him or her trace around the faces and name the plane shapes.

Name ______________________________

Sort Solid Figures

Hands On

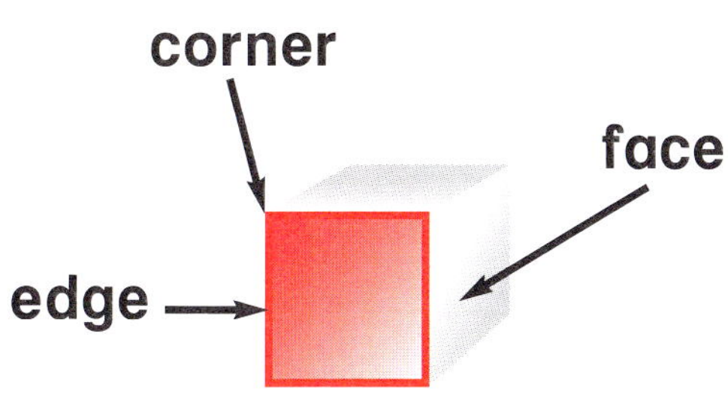

A face is a flat surface on a solid figure.
An **edge** is where two faces meet.
A corner is where the edges meet.

Use solid figures.
Sort them by the number of faces, edges, and corners. Color the correct figures.

1 0 faces, 0 edges, 0 corners

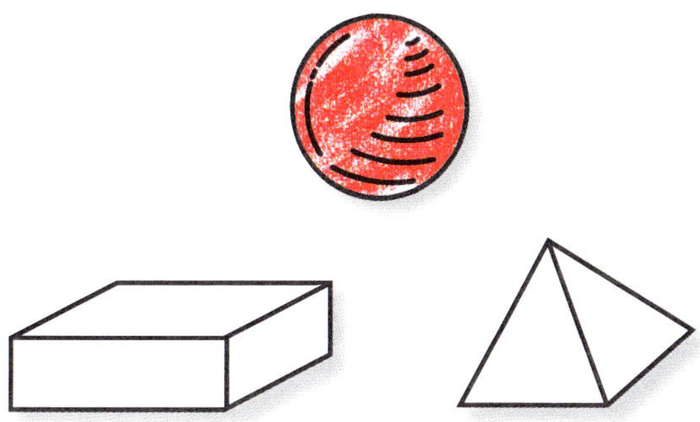

2 6 faces, 12 edges, 8 corners

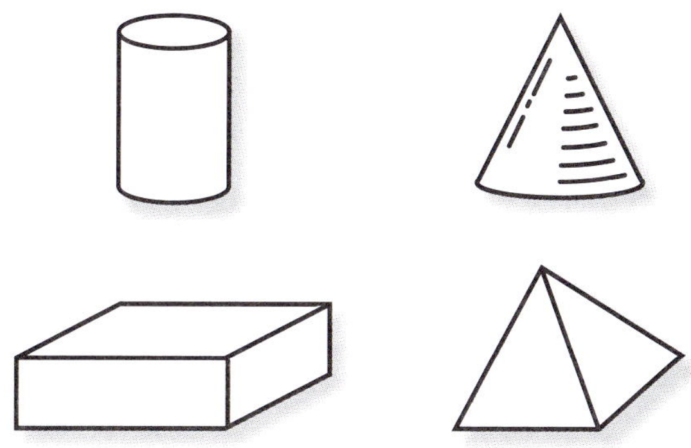

3 6 faces, 12 edges, 8 corners

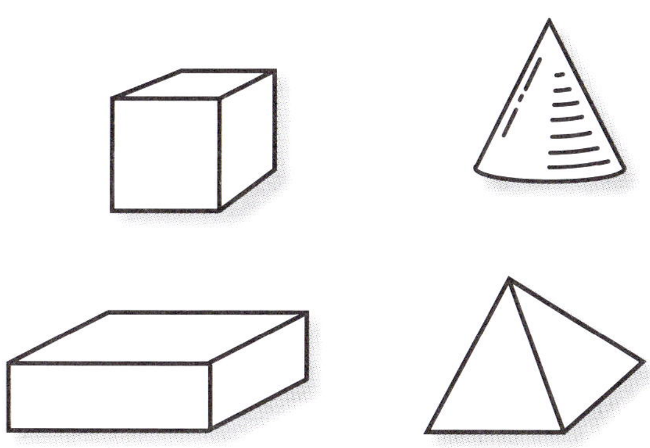

4 5 faces, 8 edges, 5 corners

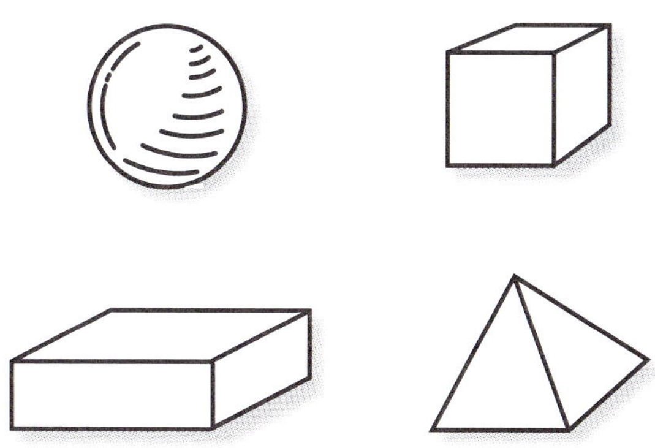

Talk About It ■ Reasoning

How are the cube and the rectangular prism alike?
How are they different?

Practice

Complete the chart. Write how many.

Solid figure	Number of faces	Number of edges	Number of corners
1  cube	6 faces	_____ edges	_____ corners
2  sphere	_____ faces	_____ edges	_____ corners
3  pyramid	_____ faces	_____ edges	_____ corners
4  rectangular prism	_____ faces	_____ edges	_____ corners

Problem Solving ■ Reasoning

5. How many faces of a cube are squares? _____

6. How many faces of a pyramid are squares? _____

7. How many faces of a pyramid are triangles? _____

HOME ACTIVITY • Gather objects from around your home that are shaped like solid figures. Have your child pick up each object, name the figure, and count how many faces, edges, and corners it has.

Name ______________________________

UNDERSTAND > PLAN > SOLVE > CHECK

Problem Solving
Make a Model

You want to make this model. About how many cubes do you think you will need?

Estimate: about ______ cubes

Build the model. How many cubes did you use?

Count: 10 cubes

Estimate the number of cubes. Then build the model. Write how many cubes you used.

1

Estimate: about ______ cubes

Count: ______ cubes

2

Estimate: about ______ cubes

Count: ______ cubes

3

Estimate: about ______ cubes

Count: ______ cubes

4

Estimate: about ______ cubes

Count: ______ cubes

Practice

Estimate the number of . Then build the model. Write how many  you used.

1

Estimate: about ______ cubes

Count: 12 cubes

2

Estimate: about ______ cubes

Count: ______ cubes

3

Estimate: about ______ cubes

Count: ______ cubes

4

Estimate: about ______ cubes

Count: ______ cubes

5

Estimate: about ______ cubes

Count: ______ cubes

6

Estimate: about ______ cubes

Count: ______ cubes

Math Journal

Write About It

Look at the model in exercise 3. Explain how you estimated how many cubes you needed to build the model.

HOME ACTIVITY • Ask your child to make a model from blocks or toy bricks at home. Have your child estimate and then count the number of items in each model.

Name ______________________________

Review/Test
Chapter 18

CHECK ■ Concepts and Skills

Color the objects that are close to the shape of the solid figure. Cross out the objects that are not shaped like the solid figure.

1 

2 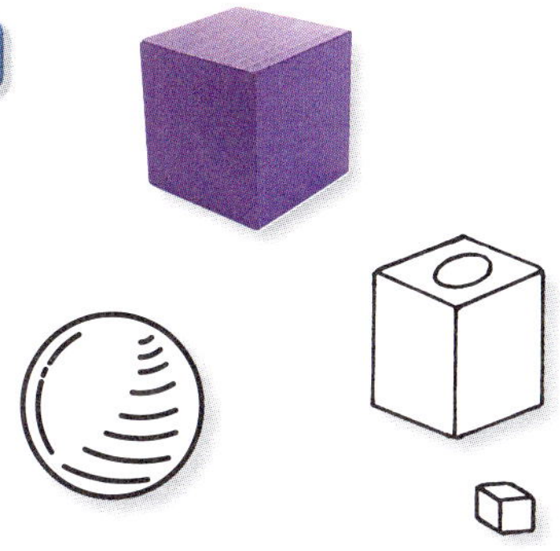

3 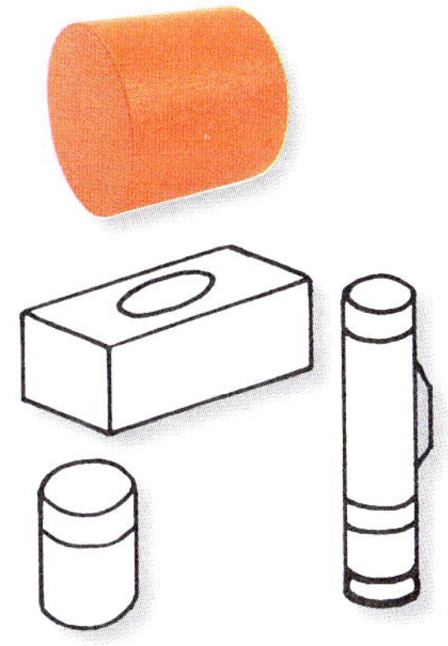

Circle the plane shape you can trace from the solid figure.

4 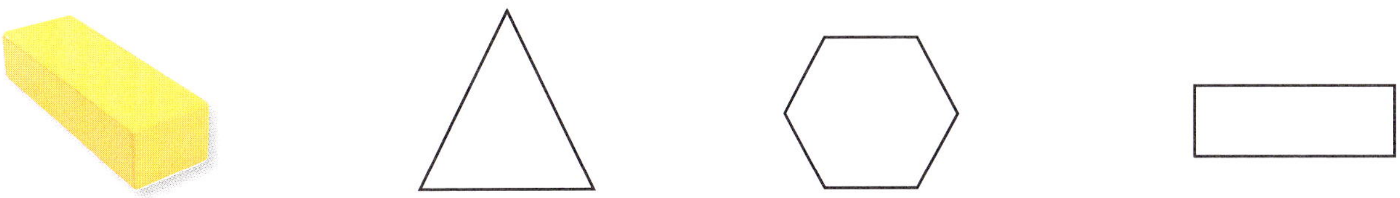

Use solid figures.
Sort them by the number of faces, edges, and corners.
Color the correct figures.

5 0 faces, 0 edges, 0 corners

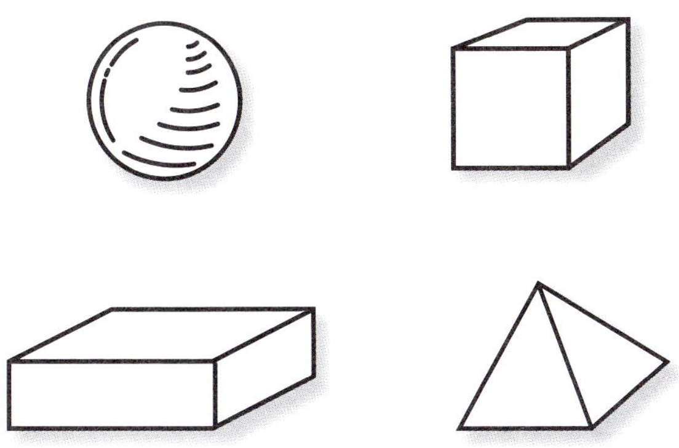

6 5 faces, 8 edges, 5 corners

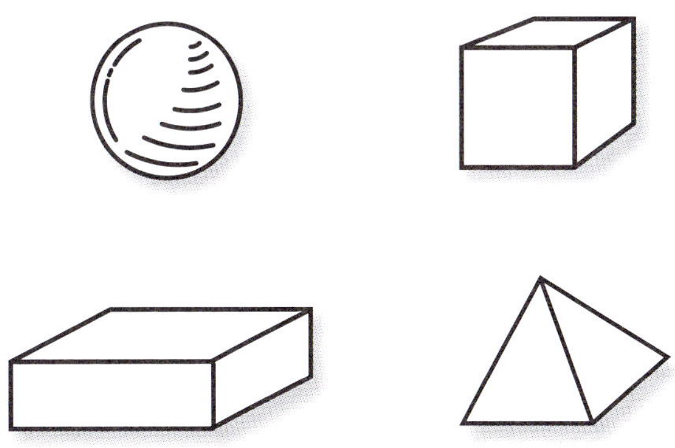

CHECK ■ Problem Solving

7 Estimate the number of .
Then build the model.
Write how many  you used.

Estimate: about ______ cubes

Count: ______ cubes

Name ______________________________

Choose the best answer for questions 1–4.

Standardized Test Prep
Chapters 1–18

1 Which object is close to the shape of this solid figure? 

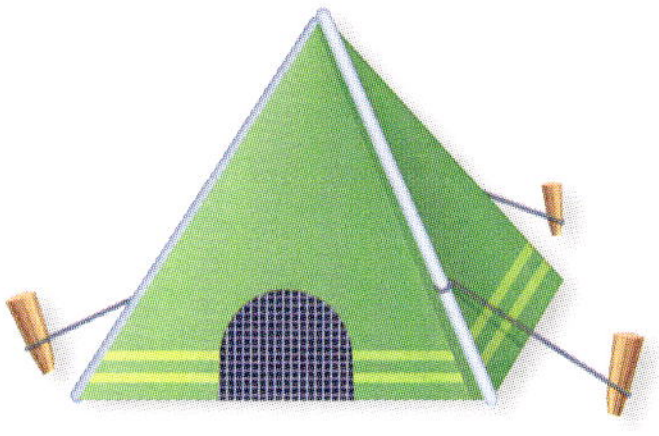

○ ○ ○ ○

2 Which is the same shape as a face of this solid figure? 

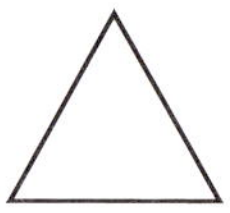

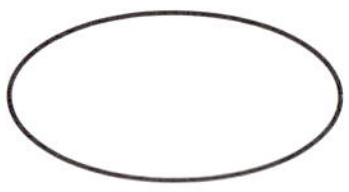
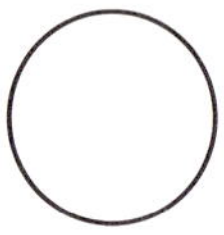

○ ○ ○ ○

3 How many  will you need to make this model?

5 ○ 6 ○ 8 ○ 9 ○

4 Which number is odd?

4 ○ 8 ○ 12 ○ 15 ○

Show What You Know

5 Choose a solid figure. Write its name.

____

Trace one face.

Write how many faces, edges, and corners it has.

______ faces

______ edges

______ corners

CHAPTER 19

Length

How long are the dinosaurs in this picture? Use string and a ruler to find out.

SCHOOL HOME CONNECTION

Dear Family,

Today we started Chapter 19. We will look at ways to measure length. Here is the math vocabulary and an activity for us to do together at home.

Love,

____

My Math Words

inch
foot
centimeter
meter

Vocabulary

inch A unit to measure short lengths. A paper clip is about 1 inch long.

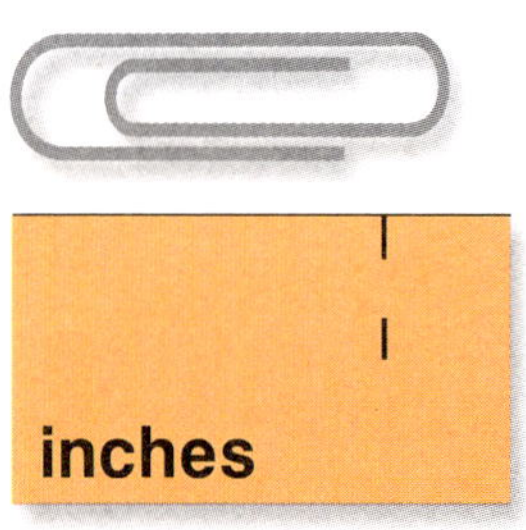

foot A unit to measure longer lengths. A sheet of notebook paper is about 1 foot long.

centimeter A unit to measure short lengths. Your finger is about 1 centimeter wide.

meter A unit to measure longer lengths. Your arms can spread about 1 meter wide.

Visit *The Learning Site* for additional ideas and activities. www.harcourtschool.com

ACTIVITY

Have your child practice measuring length by finding the height of each family member. First, use a ruler, a yardstick, or a tape measure to measure how tall your child is in inches. Write the measurement. Next, help your child measure and write how tall you are. Together, measure other family members and pets and write their heights.

Books to Share

To read about measurement with your child, look for these books in your local library.

Measuring Penny,
by Loreen Leedy,
Henry Holt, 1998.

Inch by Inch,
by Leo Lioni,
William Morrow
& Company, 1995.

Name ______________________________

Nonstandard Units

Measure the bone with a large clip.
About how many clips long is it?
Measure again with a small clip.
About how many clips long is it?

1

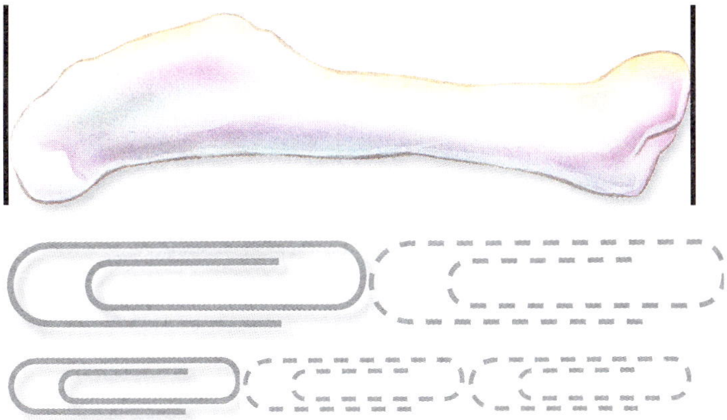

about 2 large clips

about 3 small clips

2

about ______ large clips

about ______ small clips

3

about ______ large clips

about ______ small clips

4

about ______ large clip

about ______ small clips

Talk About It ■ Reasoning

Why do you get a greater number when you measure with small paper clips?

Practice

About how many small clips long is the bone?
Predict. Then measure with a small clip to check.

1. 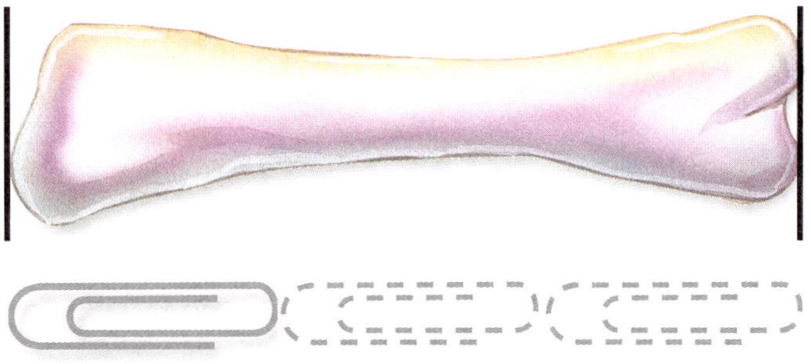

Predict: about 3 small clips

Check: about 3 small clips

2. 

Predict: about ______ small clips

Check: about ______ small clips

3. 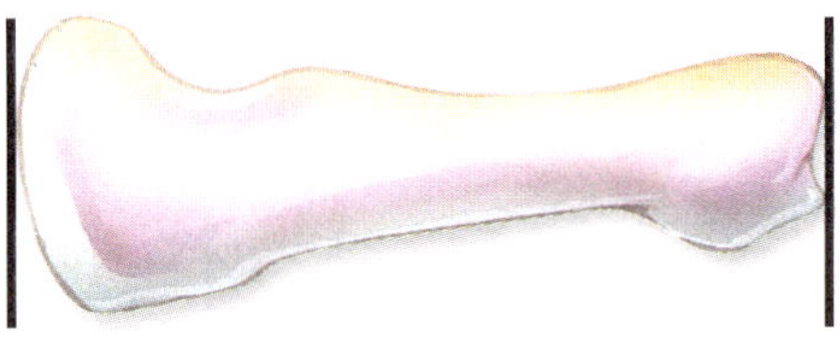

Predict: about ______ small clips

Check: about ______ small clips

4. 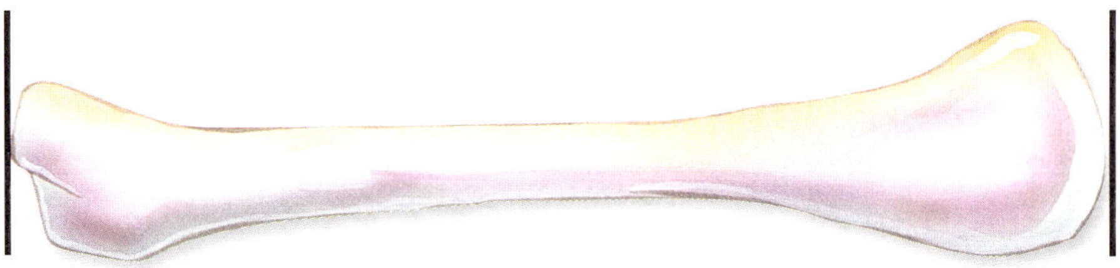

Predict: about ______ small clips

Check: about ______ small clips

HOME ACTIVITY • Have your child use other small items that are all alike to measure each dinosaur bone.

Name ______________________________

Measure to the Nearest Inch

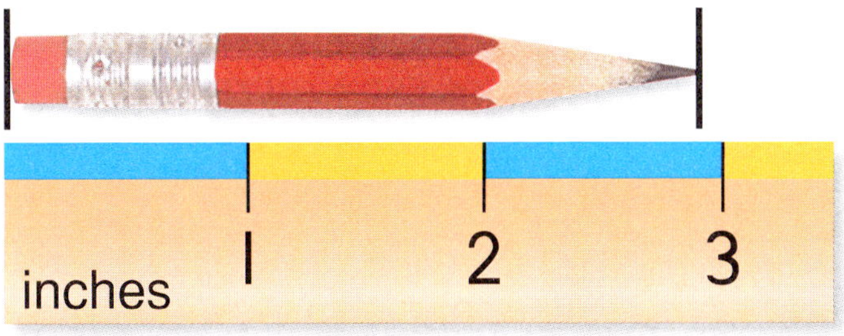

The pencil is a little less than 3 inches long, so 3 is the nearest **inch**.

about ___3___ inches

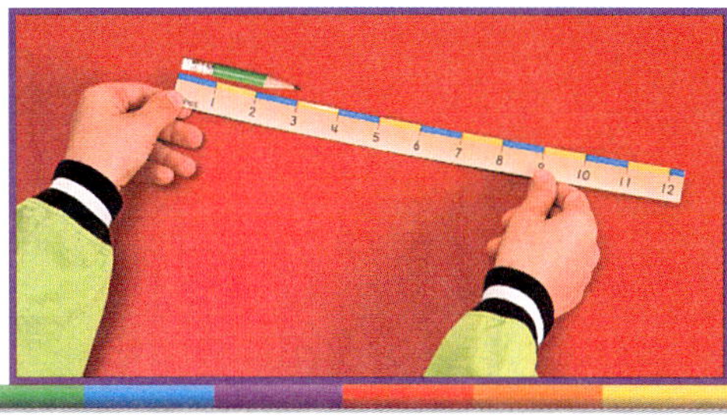

Be sure to place your ruler correctly.
Use an inch ruler. Write the length of the tool.

1

about ______ inches

2

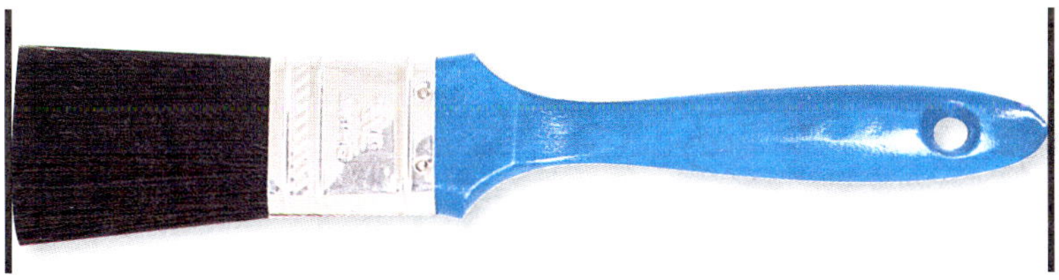

about ______ inches

3

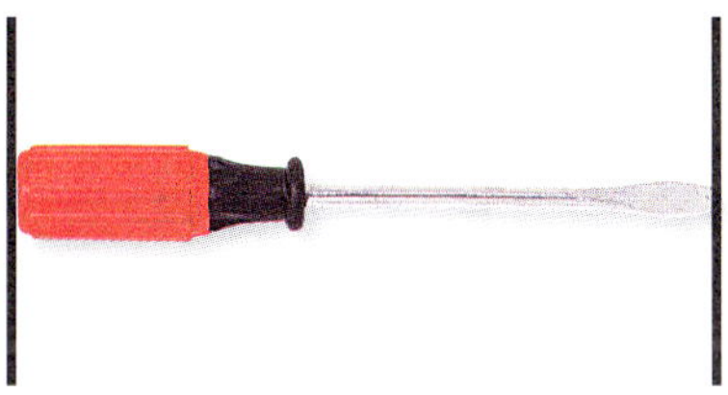

about ______ inches

4

about ______ inches

Talk About It ■ Reasoning

How do you know which inch is the nearest inch?

Practice

Work with a partner.
Use an inch ruler to measure.

Measuring Me	
1 little finger 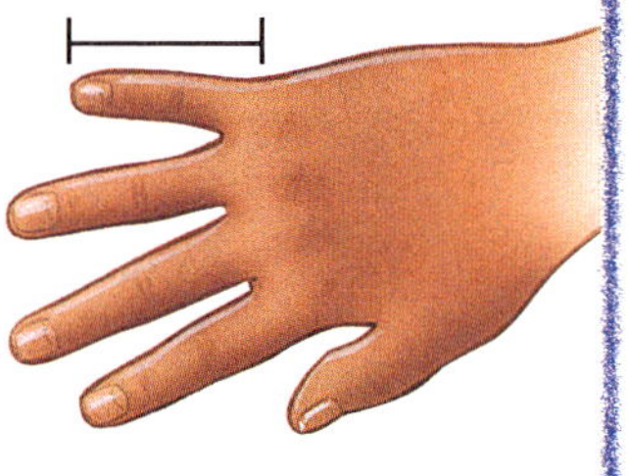 about ______ inches	2 thumb 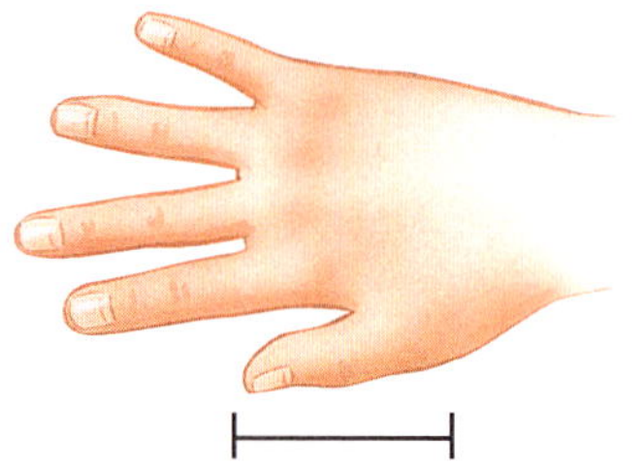 about ______ inches
3 ear 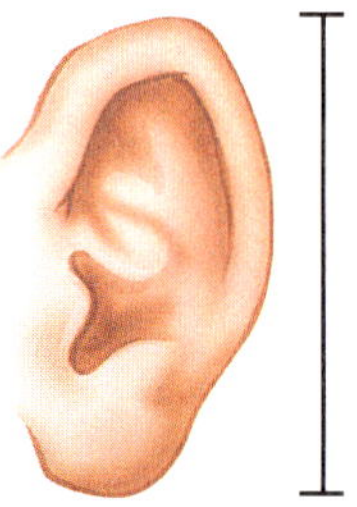 about ______ inches	4 hand 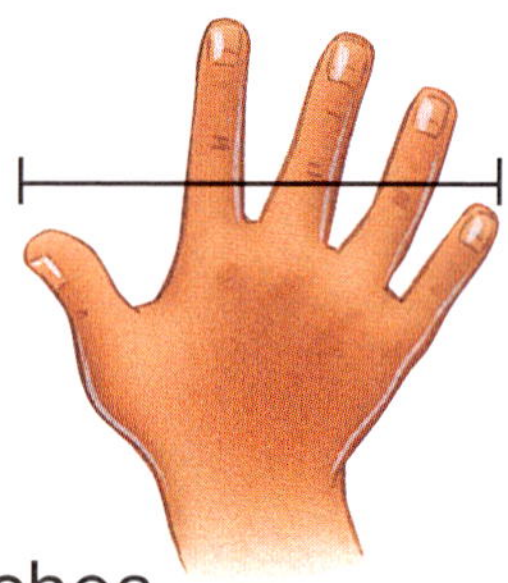 about ______ inches
5 heel to toe  about ______ inches	6 elbow to wrist 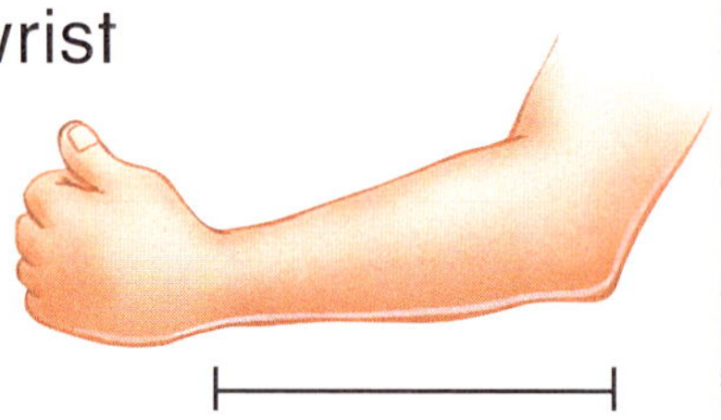 about ______ inches

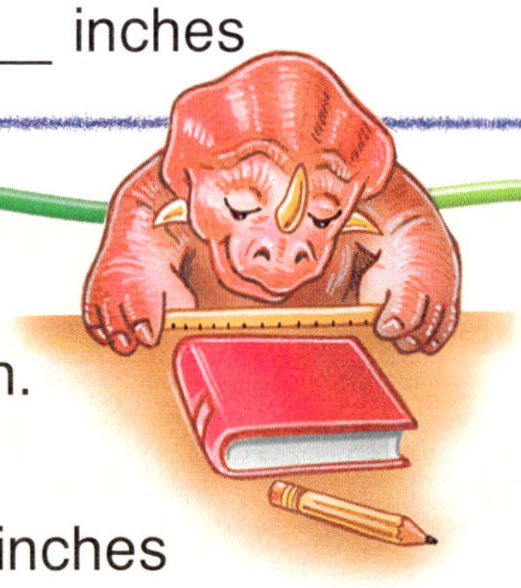

Problem Solving ■ Number Sense

Find two items in your classroom to match each length.
Draw the items.

7 about 5 inches

8 about 10 inches

HOME ACTIVITY • **Have your child use an inch ruler to measure small objects to the nearest inch.**

Name ______________________________

Inches and Feet

Measure short lengths in inches.

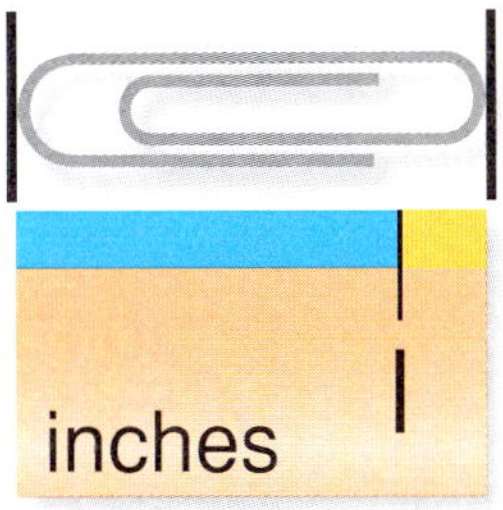

A small paper clip is about 1 inch long.

Measure longer lengths in **feet**.

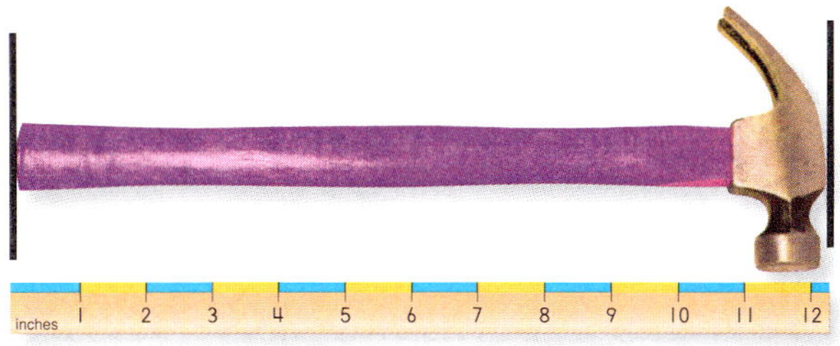

A hammer is about 1 foot long.
1 foot is 12 inches long.

About how long or high is the real object?
Estimate. Then measure with an inch ruler.

	object	estimate	measurement
1		about ______ inches	about __2__ inches
2		about ______ feet	about ______ feet
3		about ______ feet	about ______ feet
4		about ______ inches	about ______ inches

Talk About It ■ **Reasoning**

How do you use the inch ruler to measure in feet? Explain.

Practice

About how long or high is the real object?
Circle the closer estimate.

1. 
   about 9 inches
   about 9 feet

2. 
   about 2 inches
   about 2 feet

3. 
   about 1 inch
   about 1 foot

4. 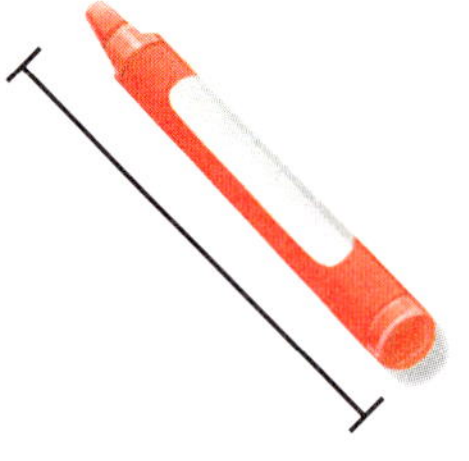
   about 4 inches
   about 4 feet

5. 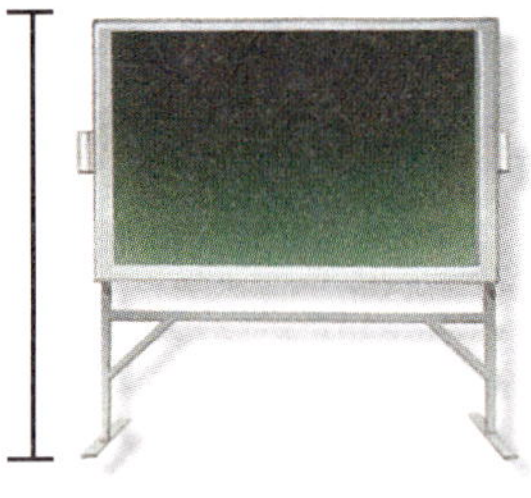
   about 5 inches
   about 5 feet

6. 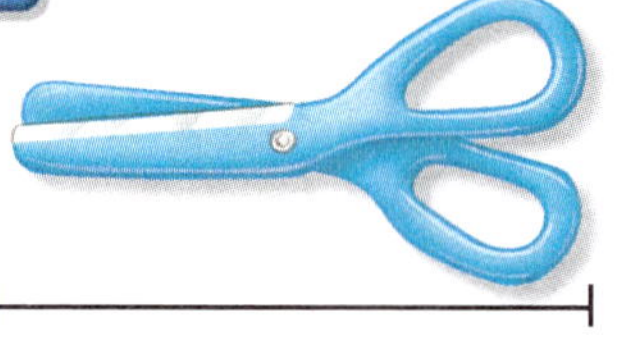
   about 4 inches
   about 4 feet

7. 
   about 6 inches
   about 6 feet

8. 
   about 6 inches
   about 6 feet

Mixed Review

Write the amount.

9. 

_____ ¢

HOME ACTIVITY • Have your child estimate the length of items around your home.

Name ______________________

Centimeters and Meters

Hands On

Measure short lengths in **centimeters**.

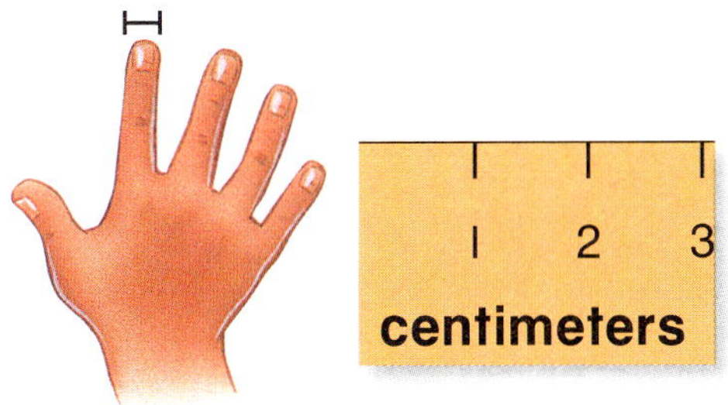

Your finger is about 1 centimeter wide.

Measure long lengths in **meters**.

Your arms can spread about 1 meter wide. 1 meter is 100 centimeters.

About how long or high is the real object? Estimate. Then measure.

	object	estimate	measurement
1	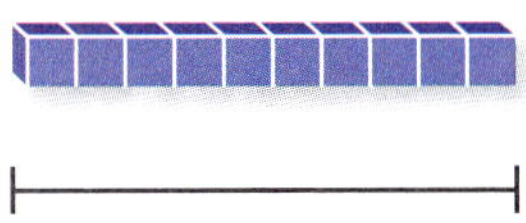	about ______ centimeters	about 10 centimeters
2		about ______ meters	about ______ meters
3	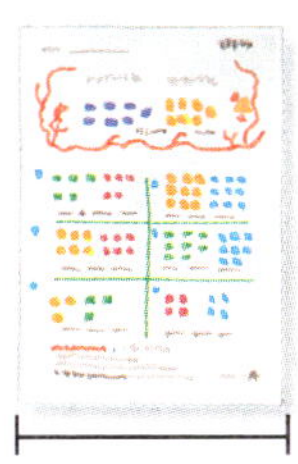	about ______ centimeters	about ______ centimeters

Talk About It ▪ Reasoning

How would your measurements change if you measured with an inch ruler? Explain.

Practice

Which unit would you use to measure the object?
Circle the better unit of measure.

1
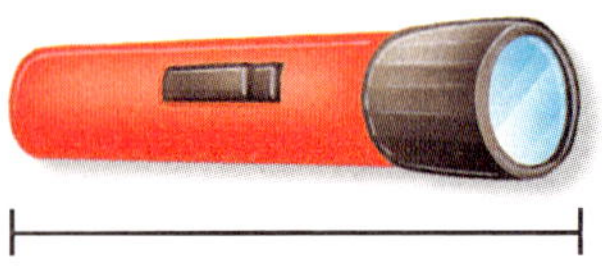
centimeters (circled)
meters

2

centimeters
meters

3
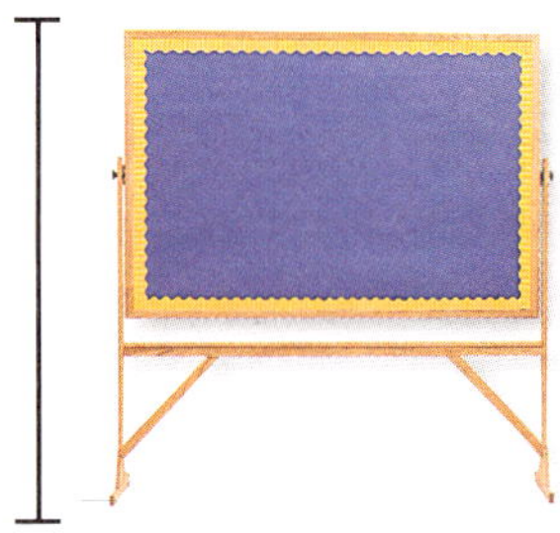
centimeters
meters

4
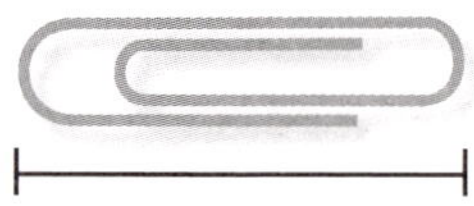
centimeters
meters

5

centimeters
meters

6

centimeters
meters

Problem Solving ■ Application

Use a centimeter ruler. Draw a line.
Start your line at the dot.

7 5 centimeters ●

8 10 centimeters ●

9 3 centimeters ●

HOME ACTIVITY • Have your child find things around your home that can be measured in centimeters. Have him or her find the length or height of each object with a centimeter ruler.

Name ______________________________

Perimeter

Use a centimeter ruler to measure each side. Write how many centimeters. Add to find the perimeter of the figure.

The distance around a figure is called the **perimeter**.

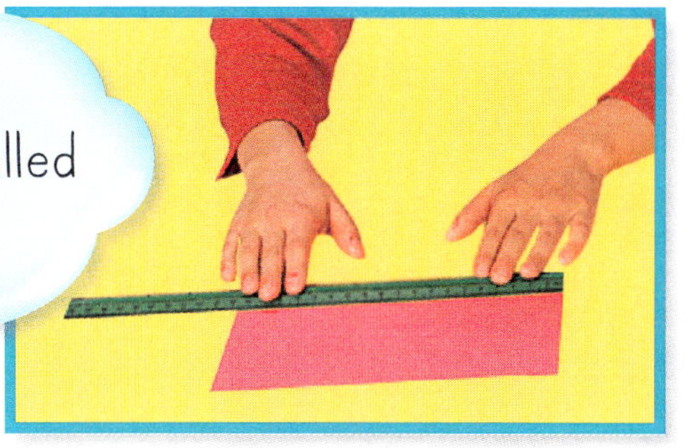

1 

4 + 2 + 4 + 2 = 12 centimeters

2 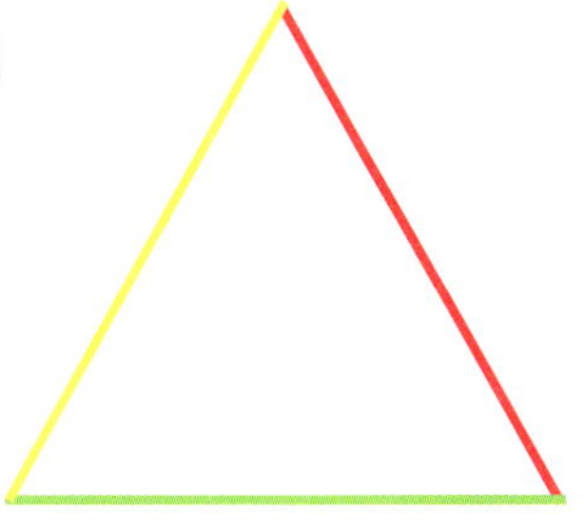

____ + ____ + ____ = ____ centimeters

3 

____ + ____ + ____ + ____ = ____ centimeters

4 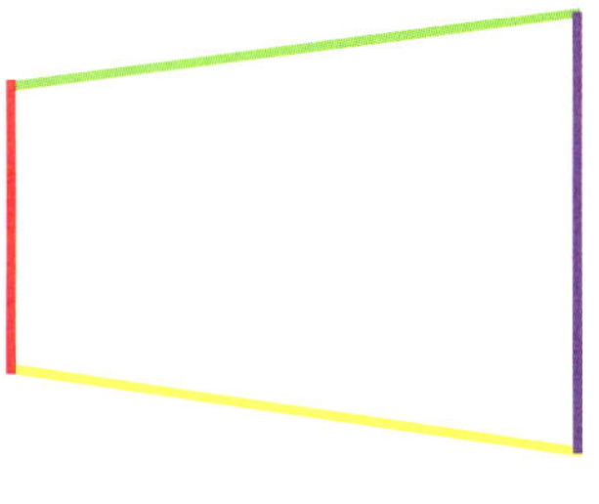

____ + ____ + ____ + ____ = ____ centimeters

Talk About It ■ **Reasoning**

How can two figures look different and have the same perimeter?

Practice

Measure each side.
Write how many centimeters.
Add to find the perimeter.

1

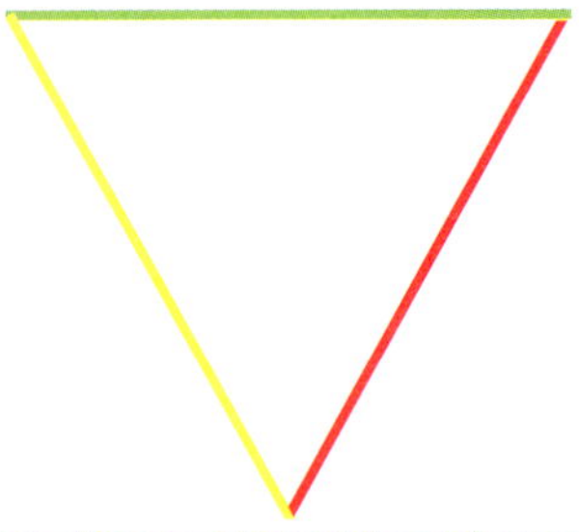

4 + 4 + 4 = 12 centimeters

2

____ + ____ + ____ + ____ = ____ centimeters

3

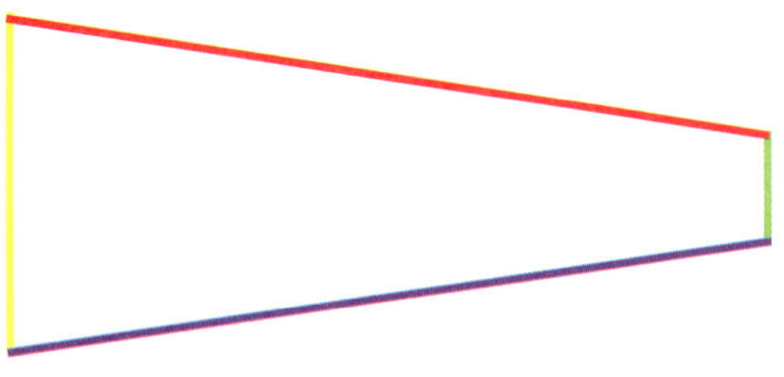

____ + ____ + ____ + ____ = ____ centimeters

Problem Solving ■ Visual Thinking

4 Draw a different figure that has the same perimeter.

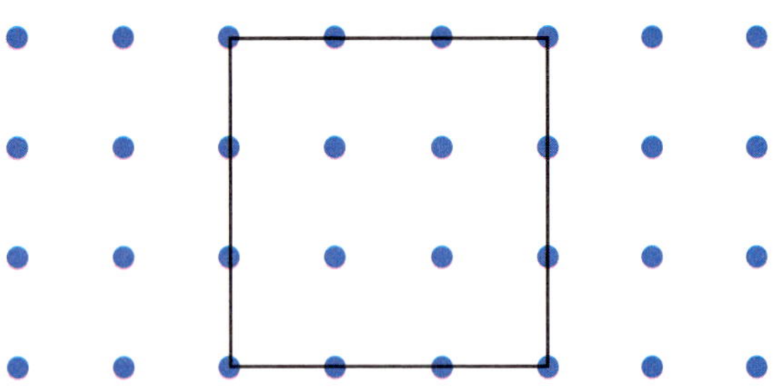

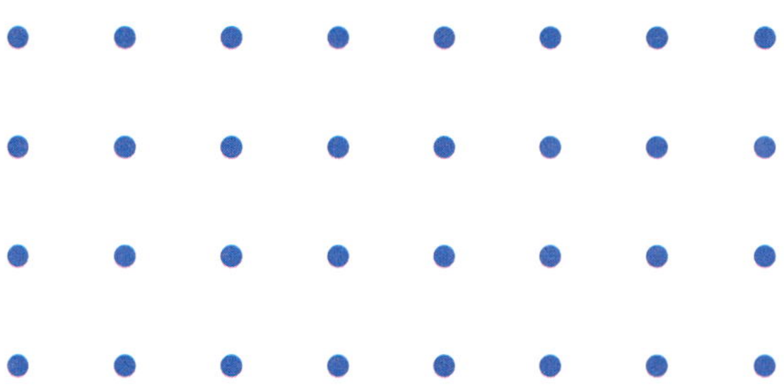

HOME ACTIVITY • Have your child measure the length of each side of a small table. Then have him or her add the lengths to find the perimeter.

Name ______________________________

UNDERSTAND › PLAN › SOLVE › CHECK

Problem Solving
Make Reasonable Estimates

Dee has this toy dinosaur.
About how long is it?
Circle the most reasonable estimate.

An estimate is reasonable if it makes sense.

Look at the length of 1 inch. Estimate how many inches would cover the length of the dinosaur.

(about 3 inches) about 5 inches about 7 inches

About how long is the toy dinosaur?
Circle the most reasonable estimate.

1

about 2 inches about 4 inches about 6 inches

2

about 2 inches about 3 inches about 5 inches

Practice

About how long is the toy dinosaur?
Circle the most reasonable estimate.

1

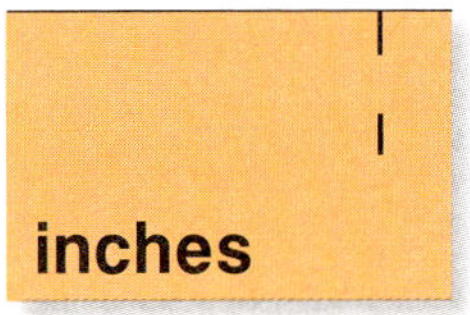

about 3 inches   about 6 inches   about 10 inches

2

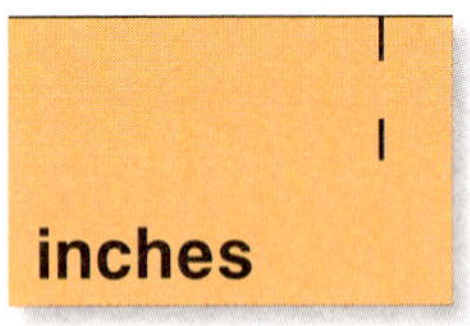

about 2 inches   about 6 inches   about 8 inches

3

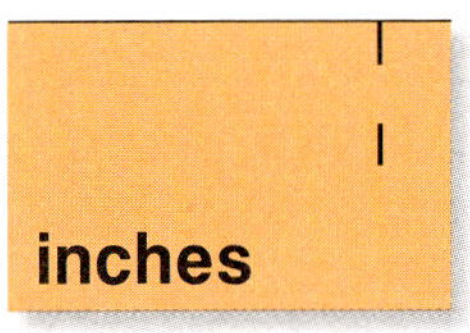

about 2 inches   about 4 inches   about 7 inches

Write About It

When might you need to estimate length?
Write a story about such a time.

HOME ACTIVITY • Ask your child to estimate the length of objects around the house. Suggest that he or she hold a one-inch piece of string at one end of the object to help in making the estimate.

Review/Test
Chapter 19

Name ______________________________

CHECK ■ Concepts and Skills

About how many clips long is the bone?

1

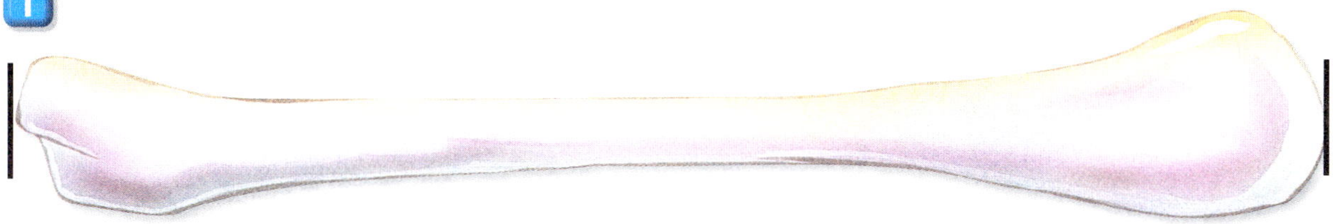

about ______ large clips   about ______ small clips

Use an inch ruler. Write the length.

2

about ______ inches

3

about ______ inches

Circle the better unit to measure the real object.

4

centimeters

meters

5

centimeters

meters

Use a centimeter ruler to measure each side. Write how many centimeters.
Add to find the perimeter.

6

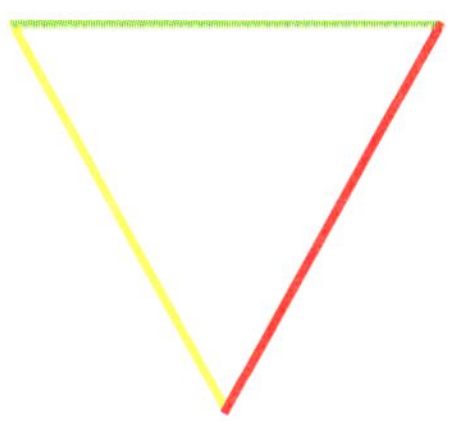

______ + ______ + ______ = ______ centimeters

CHECK ■ Problem Solving

About how long is the ribbon?
Circle the most reasonable estimate.

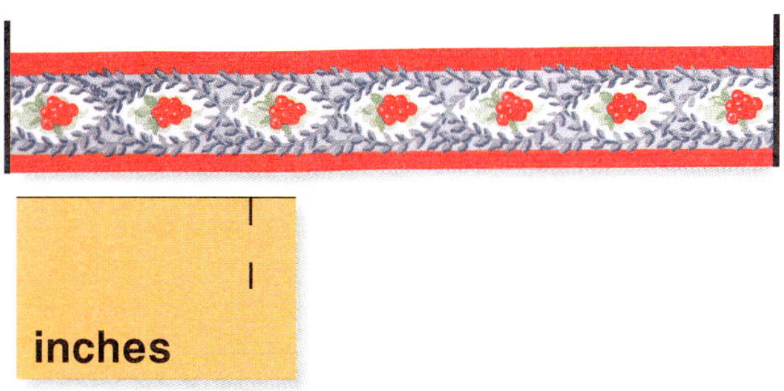

7 about 3 inches   about 5 inches   about 9 inches

Name ______________________________

Standardized Test Prep
Chapters 1–19

Choose the best answer for questions 1–3.

1 About how many clips long is the shoelace?

3	4	5	6
○	○	○	○

2 About how long is the caterpillar?

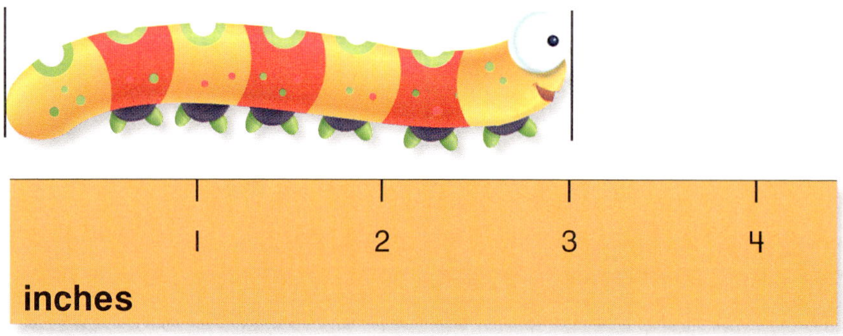

1 inch	2 inches	3 inches	4 inches
○	○	○	○

3 Which object might be 7 feet high?

○	○	○	○

Show What You Know

4 Draw a shape that has 4 sides. Use a centimeter ruler to measure the sides. Add to find the perimeter.

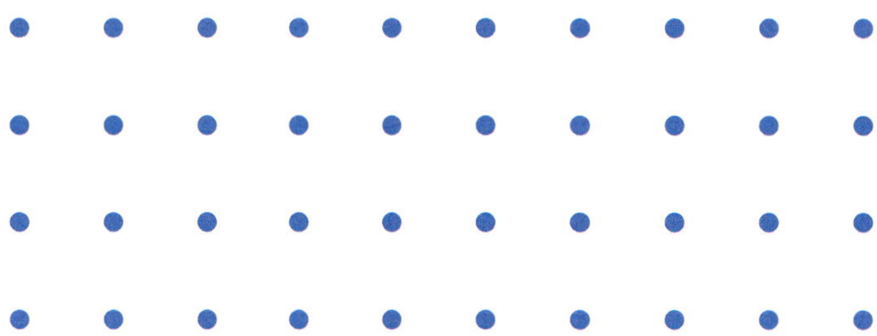

_____ + _____ + _____ + _____ = _____ centimeters

CHAPTER 20

Capacity, Weight, and Temperature

What measurement tools do you see? What would you measure with each tool?

SCHOOL HOME CONNECTION

Dear Family,

Today we started Chapter 20. We will begin to measure how much things hold, how much things weigh, and how hot or cold the weather is. Here is the math vocabulary and an activity for us to do together at home.

Love,

____

My Math Words

cup
pint
quart
liter
mass
weight

Vocabulary

Units to measure how much a container holds:	
cup	2 cups fill 1 pint
pint	2 pints fill 1 quart
quart	1 quart fills 4 cups or 2 pints
liter	1 liter is a little more than 1 quart

mass the amount of matter an object has

weight the measure of the pull of gravity on an object

ACTIVITY

At the grocery store, look for an item that weighs one pound. Let your child hold the item to get an idea of how that amount of weight feels. Then have him or her choose 10 other grocery items and estimate each weight in pounds. Check your child's estimates by reading the weights on the packages.

Books to Share

To read about measurement with your child, look for these books in your local library.

How Big Were the Dinosaurs?,
by Bernard Most,
Harcourt, Brace & Company, 1994.

Everybody Cooks Rice,
by Norah Dooley,
Houghton Mifflin, 1995.

Visit *The Learning Site* for additional ideas and activities. www.harcourtschool.com

Name ______________________________

Cups, Pints, and Quarts

Hands On

1 **cup**	1 **pint**	1 **quart**
	or 	 or 
	2 cups = 1 pint	4 cups = 1 quart

How many cups will fill the container?
Measure with water.

1 1 pint 

2 cups

2 1 quart 

______ cups

3 2 pints 

______ cups

4 2 quarts 

______ cups

Talk About It ▪ **Reasoning**

Is 1 quart equal to 2 pints? How can you tell?

Practice

About how much does the container hold?
Circle the reasonable estimate.

cup

pint

quart

1

about 8 quarts

about 50 quarts

2

about 2 pints

about 30 pints

3

about 5 cups

about 60 cups

4

about 5 quarts

about 80 quarts

5

about 3 quarts

about 13 quarts

6

about 4 pints

about 40 pints

Problem Solving ■ Application

Circle the correct sentence.

7 Mrs. Green buys 2 quarts of juice. Mrs. Little buys 4 pints of juice.

a. Mrs. Little has more juice.

b. Mrs. Little and Mrs. Green have the same amount of juice.

HOME ACTIVITY • Have your child use a measuring cup to find containers that hold the same amounts of water.

Name ______________________________

less than 1 liter **1 liter** **more than 1 liter**

About how much does the container hold?
Estimate more than, less than, or the same as 1 liter.
Write more than, less than, or same as.

1

more than 1 liter

2

______________ 1 liter

3

______________ 1 liter

4

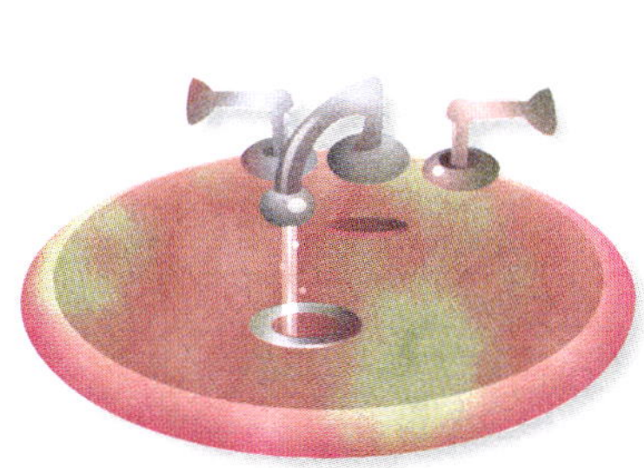

______________ 1 liter

Talk About It ■ Reasoning

How could you use a liter container and sand to find out if another container holds more or less than 1 liter?

Practice

About how much does the container hold?
Circle the reasonable estimate.

1

about 2 liters
about 20 liters

2

about 1 liter
about 10 liters

3

about 10 liters
about 60 liters

4

about 1 liter
about 10 liters

5

about 5 liters
about 20 liters

6

about 9 liters
about 90 liters

Mixed Review

7 Trace the lines.
Circle the name of the figures you made.

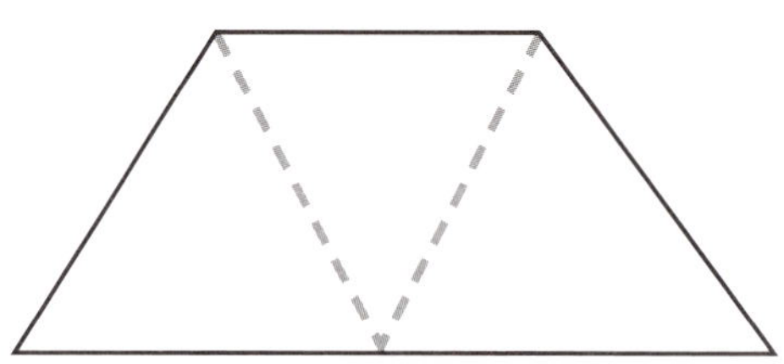

squares
triangles
rectangles

HOME ACTIVITY • Have your child find containers that he or she estimates will hold more than 1 liter, less than 1 liter, and 1 liter. Then have your child check his or her estimates by filling a liter container with water, and pouring that water into the other containers.

Name ______________________________

Ounces and Pounds

Hands On

about 1 **ounce**

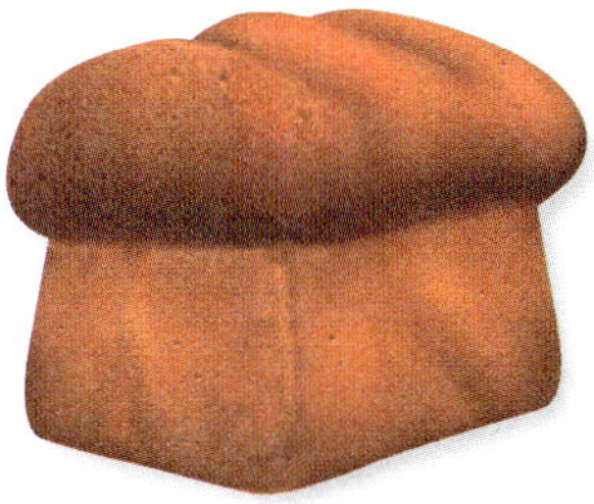

about 1 **pound**

Estimate how much the real object weighs.

1 **18 pennies**

about 2 pounds
(about 2 ounces)

2 **soccer ball**

about 3 ounces
about 3 pounds

3 **small book**

about 12 ounces
about 12 pounds

4 **toy car**

about 10 pounds
about 10 ounces

Talk About It ■ **Reasoning**

Is a large object always heavy? Explain.

Practice

Estimate how much the real object weighs.

1

about 50 pounds

about 5 ounces

2

about 9 ounces

about 9 pounds

3

about 10 pounds

about 10 ounces

4

about 8 ounces

about 8 pounds

5

about 1 pound

about 1 ounce

6

about 2 ounces

about 2 pounds

Problem Solving ■ Mental Math

Solve.

7 Latrice has a 12-pound dog. Her friend's dog weighs 20 pounds more. How many pounds do their two dogs weigh together?

_______ pounds

HOME ACTIVITY • Have your child compare the weights of three objects and put them in order from lightest to heaviest.

Name ______________________________

Grams and Kilograms

I gram

I kilogram

What is the mass of the real object?
Estimate. Then measure with a balance.

objects	estimate	measurement
1 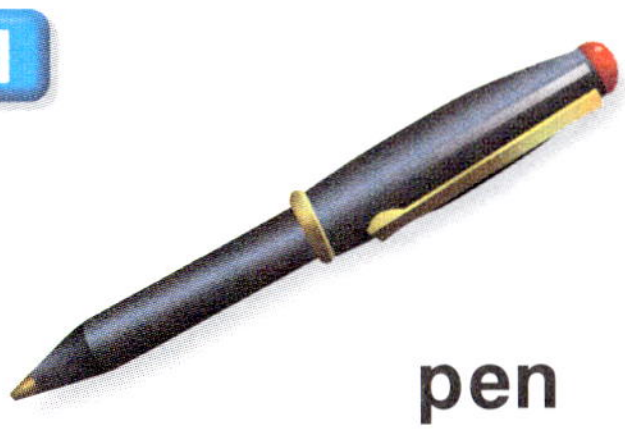 pen	about ______ grams	about ______ grams
2  backpack	about ______ kilograms	about ______ kilograms
3  quarter	about ______ grams	about ______ grams
4  wooden blocks	about ______ kilograms	about ______ kilograms

Talk About It ▪ Reasoning

About how many paper clips would
have a mass of I kilogram? Explain.

Practice

Which unit would you use to measure the mass? Circle that unit of measurement.

1

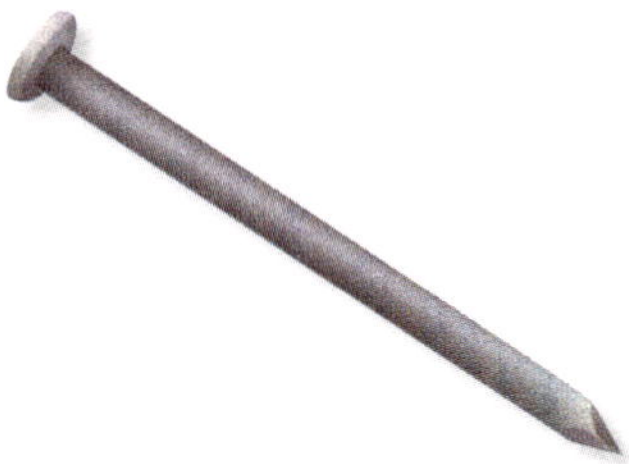

grams

liters

centimeters

2

centimeters

kilograms

grams

3

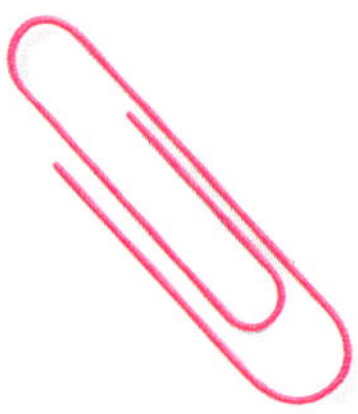

liters

meters

grams

4

centimeters

grams

kilograms

5

grams

kilograms

meters

6

grams

meters

liters

Problem Solving ■ Reasoning

Circle the reasonable answer.

7 A beagle puppy has a mass of about 1 kilogram. What might be the mass of an adult beagle?

100 kilograms   20 kilograms

8 A baby robin has a mass of about 7 grams. What might be the mass of an adult robin?

20 grams   800 grams

HOME ACTIVITY • On a trip to the supermarket, have your child find items with a mass shown in grams or kilograms. Point out that most grocery items list the mass in parentheses after the weight.

Name ______________________________

Temperature

We use a thermometer to measure the **temperature**.

We say 75 degrees Fahrenheit.

We write 75°F.

Read the thermometer.
Write the temperature.

1 **winter**

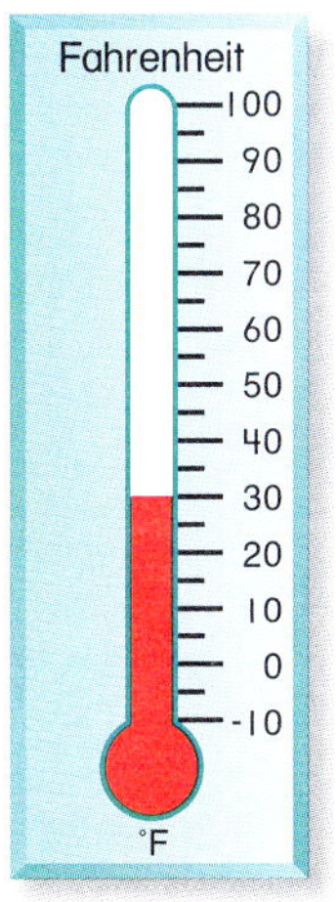

30 °F

2 **spring**

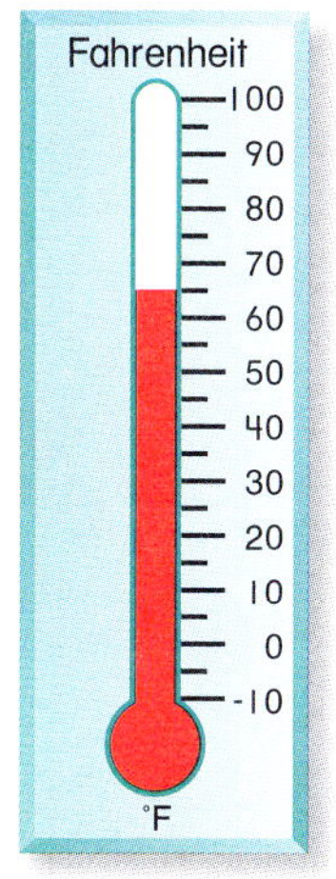

______ °F

3 **summer**

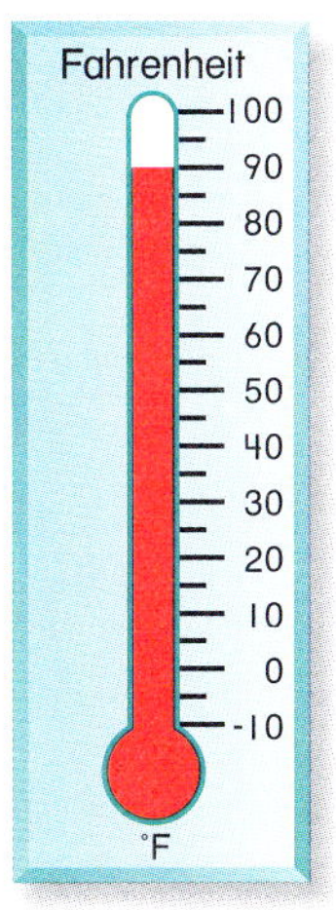

______ °F

4 **fall**

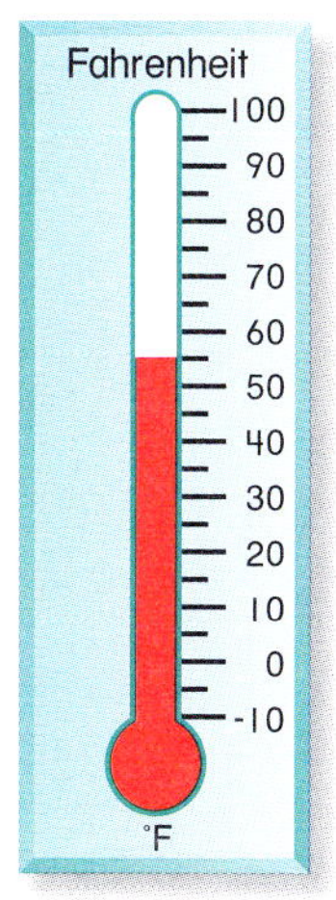

______ °F

Talk About It ■ Reasoning

What temperature do you think an outside thermometer would show today?

Practice

Read the temperature.
Use a red crayon to color the thermometer to show the temperature.

1. 80°F

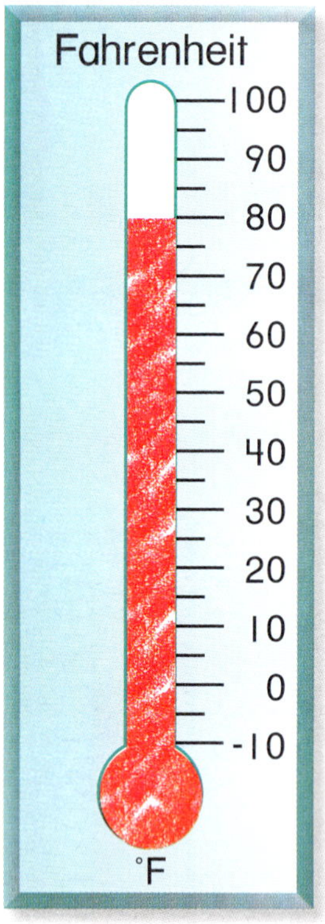

2. 25°F

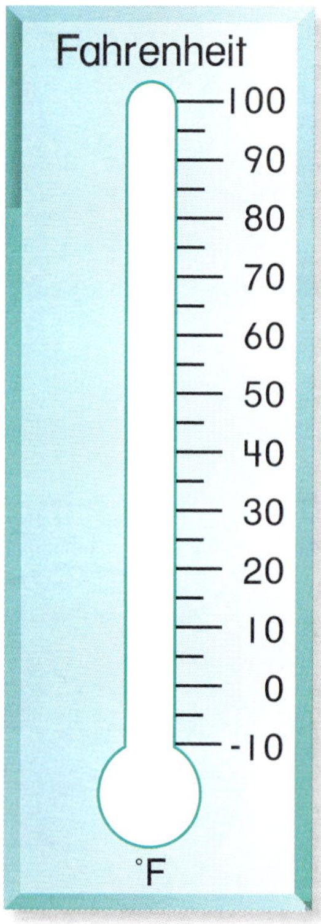

3. 40°F

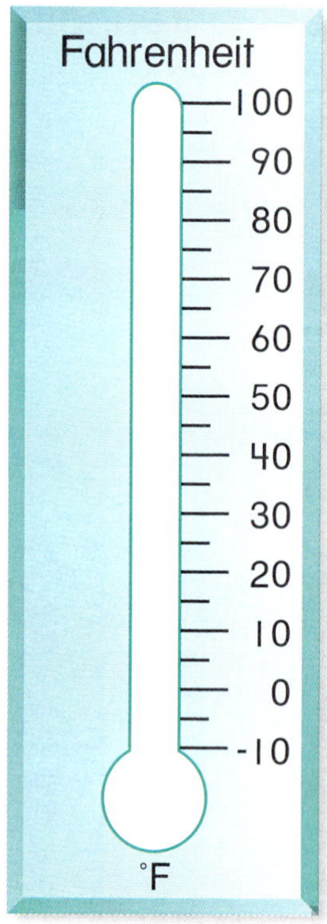

4. 95°F

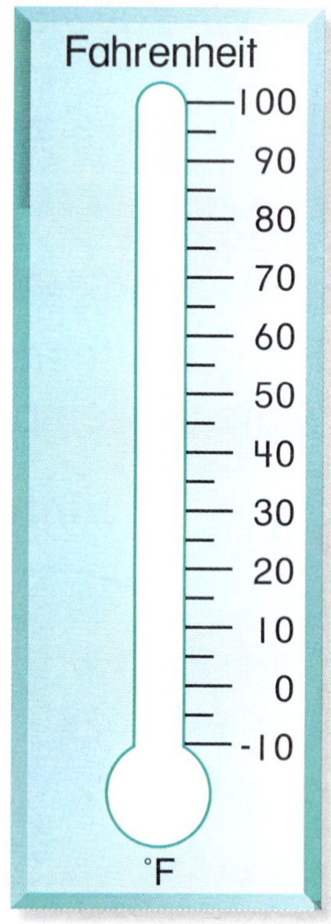

Problem Solving ■ Visual Thinking

A thermometer is like a number line.
Use crayons to circle temperatures on the number line.

5. hottest temperature
6. favorite outside temperature
7. coldest temperature
8. favorite inside temperature

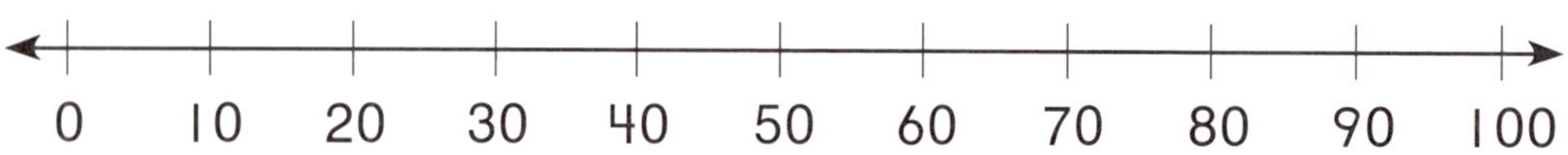

HOME ACTIVITY • Have your child read a thermometer and tell you the temperature.

Name ____________________

UNDERSTAND PLAN SOLVE CHECK

Problem Solving
Choose a Measuring Tool

Write the name of the tool you would use

1. to find out how long a piece of string is. 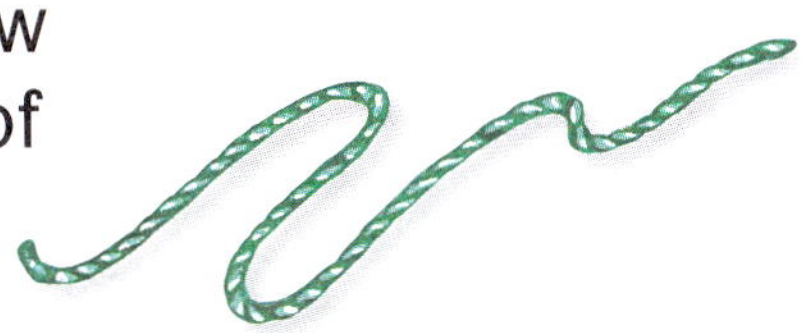 ruler
2. to find out how much water is in a bottle.  ____________________
3. to find out the temperature on a sunny day.  ____________________
4. to find out how much milk is in a pitcher.  ____________________
5. to find out how much a rock weighs. 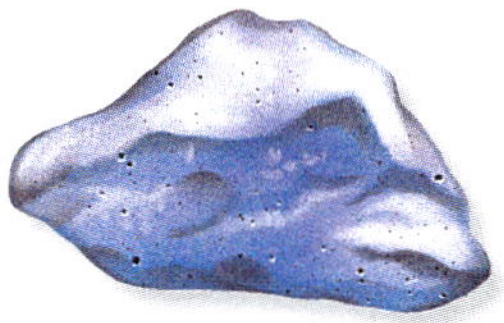 ____________________

Practice

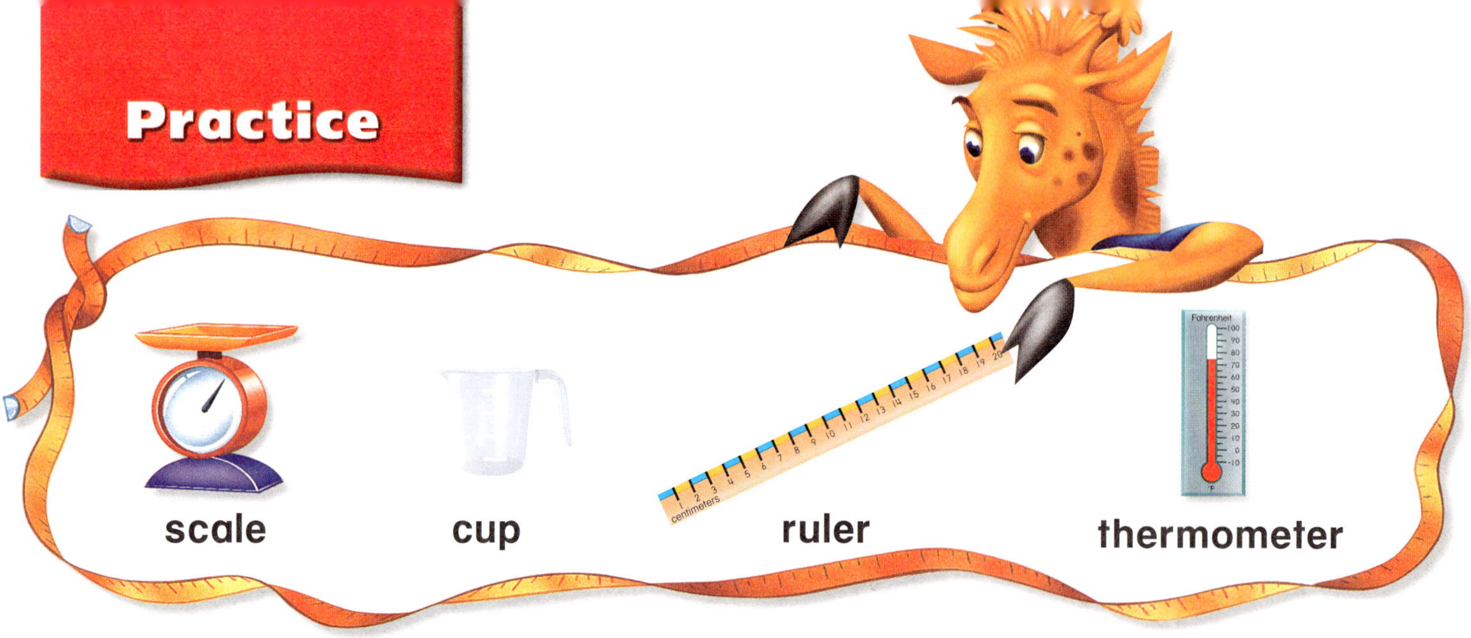

Write the name of the tool you would use

1. to find out how much your pet weighs.  scale

2. to find out how much juice is in a glass.  ________

3. to find out how long a piece of ribbon is.  ________

4. to find out the temperature of the classroom.  ________

Math Journal

Write About It

Write a sentence about each tool.
Tell what it measures.

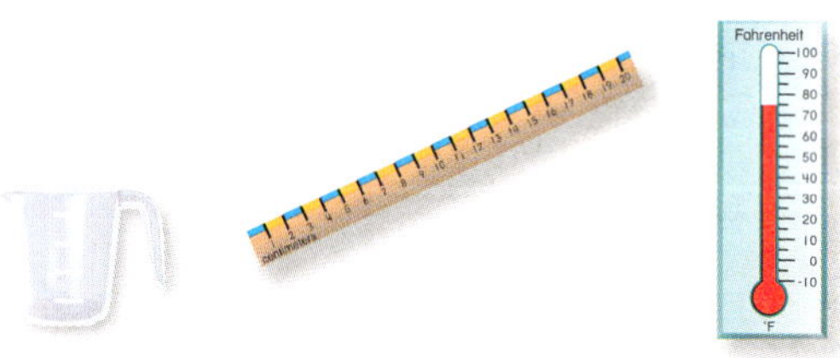

HOME ACTIVITY • Make up some stories in which a tool is needed to measure. Have your child tell you which tool he or she would use and why.

Name ______________________________

Review/Test
Chapter 20

CHECK ■ Concepts and Skills

About how much does the container hold? Circle the reasonable estimate.

1 

about 1 pint

about 10 pints

2 

about 1 quart

about 10 quarts

About how much does the container hold? Circle the reasonable estimate.

3 

2 liters

12 liters

Estimate how much the real object weighs.

4 

about 3 ounces

about 3 pounds

Which unit would you use to measure the mass? Circle that unit of measurement.

5 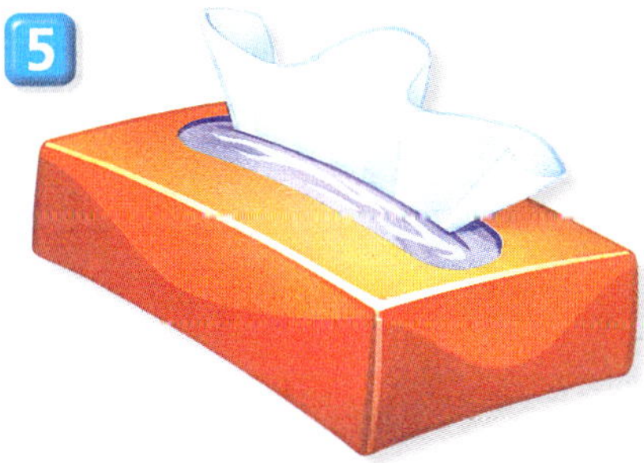

grams

kilograms

Read the thermometer. Write the temperature.

6 ______ °F

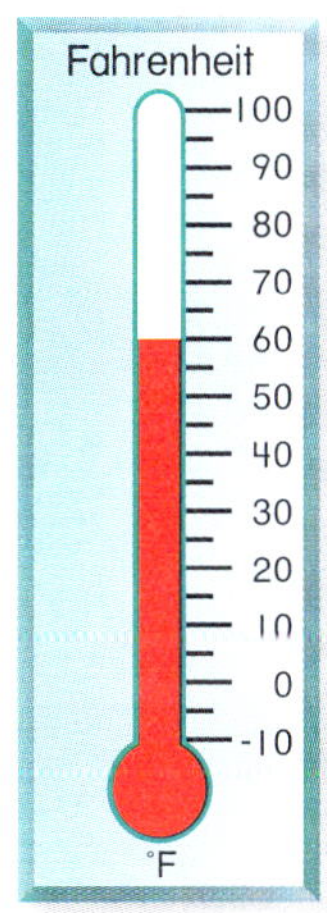

CHECK ■ Problem Solving

scale

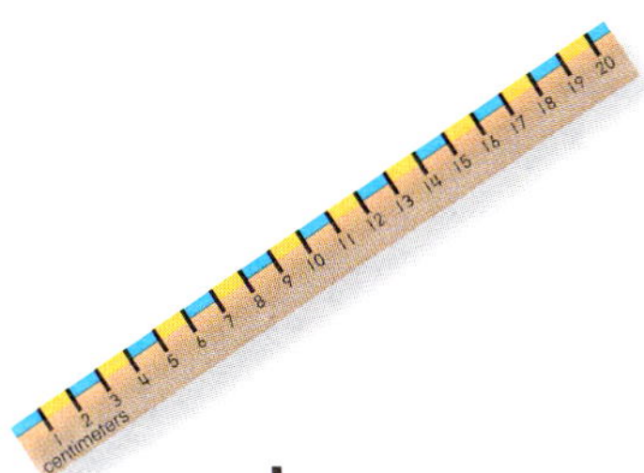

ruler

cup

thermometer

7 Write the name of the tool you would use to find out how much milk is in a bottle.

____

Name ______________________________

Choose the best answer for questions 1–4.

Standardized Test Prep
Chapters 1–20

1

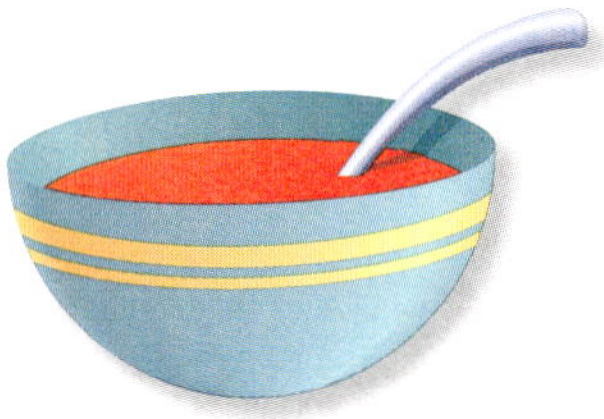

How much soup does the bowl hold?

about 2 pints	about 2 quarts	about 2 cups	about 2 gallons
○	○	○	○

2

Which unit would be used to measure the mass of a small bag of popcorn?

grams	kilograms	liters	meters
○	○	○	○

3

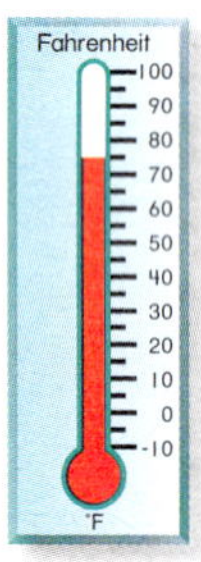

Which shows the temperature on the thermometer?

64°	65°	74°	95°
○	○	○	○

4

What would you use to find out how long the pencil is?

yardstick	scale	thermometer	ruler
○	○	○	○

Show What You Know

5 Use a container. Draw it. Estimate how many cups you think it will hold. Measure to check.

Estimate: ______ cups

Measure: ______ cups

Mrs. Quigley's Quilt

written by Lucy Floyd
illustrated by Christine Mau

This book will help me review plane shapes.

This book belongs to ____________________.

A

The winter was very cold. Mrs. Quigley decided to make a nice quilt to keep her piglets warm. First, she cut cloth squares. Then she laid out some squares on the table.

"Too many squares," said Mrs. Quigley. She put some squares together to make rectangles for her quilt.

Tell about the shapes you see in Mrs. Quigley's quilt.

"Very nice," said Mrs. Quigley. "I need another shape." She cut some squares in half to make triangles for her quilt. Then she finished sewing the shapes together.

How many triangles does she have?

______

"Perfect!" said Mrs. Quigley.
"It's big enough for all of us!"

Name ______________________

Groovy Shapes

Look at each design and write how many shapes you see.

How many ovals? ____

How many circles? ____

How many triangles? ____

How many squares? ____

How many rectangles? ____

Stretch Your Thinking ■ Create a design made from a plane shape. See if a classmate can tell how many of that shape you used.

Name ______________________________

Challenge
Probability

You will need:
9 yellow, 3 blue, 3 red, 1 bag.

1. Put all the yellow, blue, and red tiles in the bag. Pull out 1 tile. Make a tally mark to show which color you pulled out.

2. Put the tile back. Shake the bag.

3. Repeat 9 times.

Color	Tally Marks
yellow	
blue	
red	

4. If you do this 10 more times, which color do you think you will pull out most often?

   Write your prediction.

   ____

   ____

5. Repeat 10 more times. Make a tally mark each time.

6. Which color tile did you pull out most often?

   ____

7. Why do you think this happened?

   ____

   ____

   ____

   ____

Name ______________________________

Study Guide and Review

Skills and Concepts

1 Draw a square.

2 Draw the shape.

3 sides　　　3 corners

3 Draw a line of symmetry.

4 Draw lines to divide the shape into 4 triangles.

5 Circle turn or flip to tell how the shape was moved.

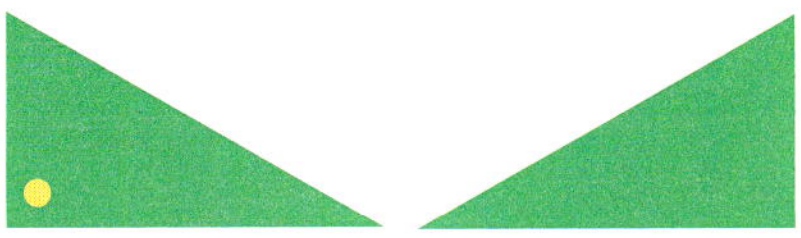

turn　　　flip

6 Circle the figures that have the same shape.

7 Circle the solid figure you can use to trace the shape.

8 Write how many.

_____ faces　　_____ edges

_____ corners

9 Use paper clips. Write the length.

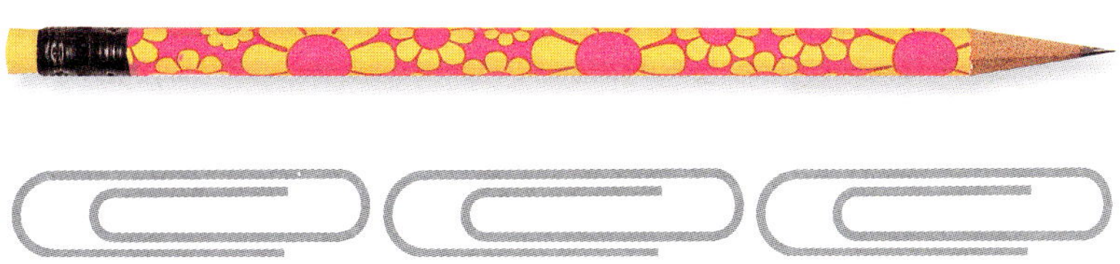

_____ clips

10 Write how many centimeters. Then write the perimeter.

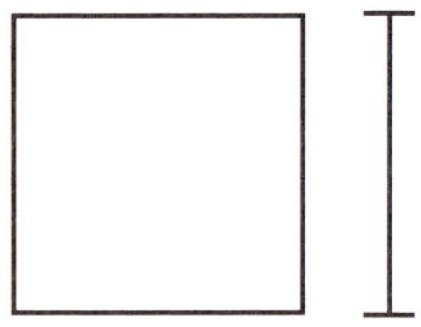

2 cm

_____ + _____ + _____ + _____ = _____

Circle the reasonable estimates.

11

about 2 liters | about 20 liters

12

about 30 quarts | about 3 quarts

13

about 1 ounce | about 1 pound

Which unit would you use to measure?
Circle the better unit of measure.

14

grams | kilograms | liters

15

centimeters | meters

Problem Solving

16 About how long is the object? Circle the most reasonable estimate.

about 6 inches | about 1 inch | about 3 inches

Name ______________________________

Ant Farm

Amy wanted to place colored tape around an ant farm.

- She had 20 inches of colored tape.
- Amy made a 4-cornered shape using all of the tape to outline the perimeter.

Draw one way the shape could look. Measure and label each side in inches.

Show your work.

Technology

Name ____

Mighty Math Zoo Zillions • Solid Figures and Plane Shapes

1. Click .

2. Click .

3. Click N.

4. Play 5 times.

Practice and Problem Solving

How many of each solid figure do you see?

1. sphere ______ cone ______

   cylinder ______ cube ______

   pyramid ______

   rectangular prism ______

2. **Reasoning**
   Which solid figure above has only 1 plane shape that can be traced? ______

Name ______________________________

PROBLEM SOLVING ON LOCATION

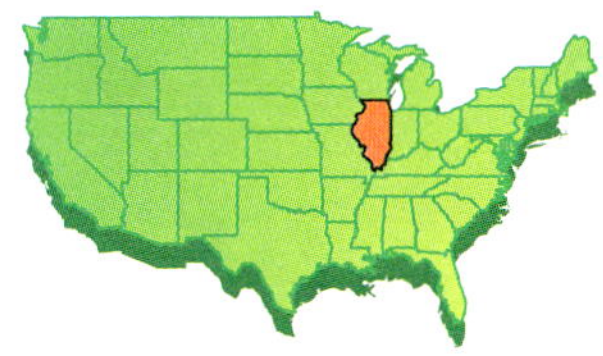

At the Museum

The Illinois State Museum has beautiful Amish quilts. They are taken from town to town so that people all around the state can see them.

This quilt has 4 small squares that make up 1 larger square. There are 5 squares in all.

Draw and color this quilt to make 14 squares in all.

This quilt has 4 small triangles that make up 2 larger triangles. There are 8 triangles in all.

Draw and color this quilt to make 16 triangles in all.

Name ______________________________

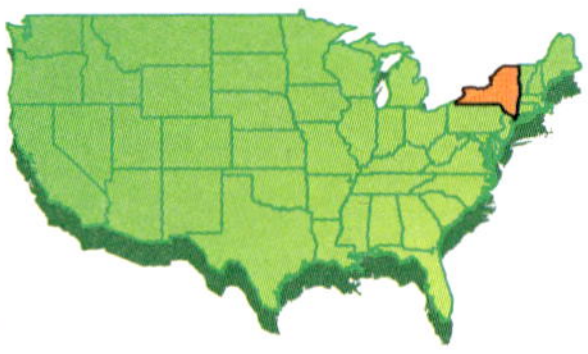

PROBLEM SOLVING ON LOCATION

At the Restaurant

People from all over the world come to New York City. They bring their recipes for great food with them.

What different kinds of pizzas can you make with these toppings?

Draw two or more toppings on each pizza. Write the name of each topping.